# CONODONTS AND ZONATION OF THE UPPER DEVONIAN IN THE GREAT BASIN

*The printing of this volume
has been made possible
through the bequest of
Richard Alexander Fullerton Penrose, Jr.*

The Geological Society of America, Inc.
Memoir 103

# CONODONTS AND ZONATION
# OF THE
# UPPER DEVONIAN IN THE GREAT BASIN

By

**DAVID L. CLARK**
*University of Wisconsin, Madison, Wisconsin*

and

**RAYMOND L. ETHINGTON**
*University of Missouri, Columbia, Missouri*

1967

Published by

THE GEOLOGICAL SOCIETY OF AMERICA, INC.
231 East 46th Street
New York, New York 10017

*Made in the United States of America*

# PREFACE

In early 1963 when this manuscript was submitted for publication, the only accounts of multiple Upper Devonian conodont zonation were those of Clark and Becker (1960) for parts of the Great Basin, Collinson and others (1962) for the mid-continent, and the various German reports, the most important being that by Ziegler (1962b). The completed manuscript of this report recorded confirmation of Devonian conodont zones outside of Germany and presented complete synonymies and descriptions in English of many important species. From that date to publication, many important papers on Upper Devonian conodonts have appeared. A partial revision to include the most important new references has been accomplished.

# ACKNOWLEDGMENTS

Many specimens described in this report were collected as part of a study supported by a grant from the Penrose Bequest of The Geological Society of America. J. H. Becker made preliminary identification of part of the fauna as a Southern Methodist University M. S. thesis and spent part of the summer of 1958 doing field work for this project. J. E. Brooks of Southern Methodist University aided in field determinations and contributed some stratigraphic data for the Pilot Shale. G. A. Beach (1961) collected samples from the Upper Devonian Pinyon Peak and Fitchville formations for a Brigham Young University M. S. thesis. Some specimens which he obtained were also used. J. Fred Smith of the U. S. Geological Survey conducted the writers to critical localities in the eugeosynclinal Upper Devonian and, with Keith Ketner, supplied other samples from north-central Nevada. J. K. Rigby and H. J. Bissell aided in field studies.

Additional field work and time for completion of this study have been made possible by grants G-19726 and GP-3585 from the National Science Foundation. Funds from the National Science Foundation were also used in partially defraying costs of publication.

# CONTENTS

## FIGURES

## PLATES

## TABLES

# ABSTRACT

Studies of Upper Devonian rocks in western Utah and central and eastern Nevada have determined the presence of 101 species of 25 conodont genera. The description of this fauna, which includes a new species of *Palmatolepis?*, has led to the recognition of distinct conodont assemblages and zones which are considerably more refined than previous classifications in this area.

Representatives of nine of the ten major Upper Devonian conodont zones which have been defined in Germany can be recognized in the Great Basin rocks. These zones are, from oldest to youngest, the *dubia* (= *asymmetrica?*), *Ancyrognathus triangularis, gigas, Palmatolepis triangularis, crepida, rhomboidea, quadrantinodosa, velifera*, and the *costatus*. In Germany, Ziegler (1962b) has recognized 24 subdivisions of the ten major zones. Elements of ten of the first 15 subdivisions (lower and middle Upper Devonian) and two of the upper nine subdivisions (upper Upper Devonian) have been identified in Utah and Nevada. The uppermost part of the Devonian has yielded the most meager faunas in the Great Basin rocks.

The distinctiveness of many of the German zones is based on first and last occurrences of apparently phylogenetically related conodont "species." Similar occurrences are recognized in the Great Basin rocks, but, in general, conodonts are less numerous in these geosynclinal sequences than in the German sections. This is probably due, in part, to the distribution of conodonts through a greater thickness of sediment in the Great Basin.

The lowest zone recognized is considered the base of the Upper Devonian and is characterized by the same assemblage used to designate the middle *dubia* (= *asymmetrica?*) zone in Germany. In Nevada, 34 species have been identified in this assemblage, of which only four occur in younger rocks. Most important elements of this assemblage are the name species, *Polygnathus dubia asymmetrica* Bischoff and Ziegler, *P. dubia Hinde* (= *P. asymmetrica ovalis* Ziegler and Klapper?), *Ancyrodella rotundiloba* (Bryant), and *Palmatolepis? ziegleri* n. sp. This fauna has been identified in the lower part of the upper Devils Gate Limestone in central Nevada and in an unnamed formation in north-central Nevada from which thousands of specimens have been recovered.

The *Ancyrognathus triangularis* zone has been recognized above the *dubia* (= *asymmetrica?*) zone in the Devils Gate Limestone in central Nevada, in the uppermost beds of the Guilmette Formation in western Utah, and in the lower beds of the Pilot Shale in this same area. The species identified include the name species and *Palmatolepis foliacea*, which is most important for the zone identification.

Both the lower and upper *gigas* zones can be distinguished in the Pilot Shale of western Utah where 15 species are identified in the lower part and six species in the upper. Species of *Palmatolepis*, including *P. unicornis* in the lower zone and *P. linguiformis* in the upper, aid in recognition of these divisions.

The three divisions of the *Palmatolepis triangularis* zone recognized in Germany can be identified in the Devils Gate Limestone and the Pilot Shale. The lower division is characterized by the first occurrence of the name species before the occurrence of palmatolepid species which are present in the overlying zone. The middle division assemblage consists of 21 species, nine of which are recognized only in this zone. The upper division has been identified by the presence of 22 species, including six species of *Palmatolepis*.

Only the lower division of the *crepida* zone is recognized in the Great Basin and this is done on the occurrence of 18 species, more than half of which are present in other zones as well. Specimens of *P. quadrantinodosalobata* of the type identified in Germany (Ziegler, 1962b, p. 28) aid in the determination of this zone.

The *rhomboidea* zone is well developed in the upper beds of the Devils Gate Formation where seven species of *Palmatolepis* not recognized in higher or lower intervals plus five other species are present.

The lower *quadrantinodosa* zone has been recognized in a single sample of the Pilot Shale of western Utah but this sample includes the diagnostic *P. quadrantinodosa inflexa*.

The *velifera* zone is distinguished by the presence of *Palmatolepis rugosa trachytera* and five other species which have been found in several samples of the Pinyon Peak Limestone of central Utah. The highest conodont zone recognized includes *Polygnathus vogesi* and *Spathognathodus aculeatus* which are indicative of the middle *costatus* zone in Germany. These two species occur in the lower beds of the Fitchville Formation in central Utah.

The presence of conspecific conodonts in the same sequence as that found elsewhere confirms the widespread biostratigraphic value of the multiple Upper Devonian zonation which was first well defined in Germany.

# INTRODUCTION

The first attempt at a conodont zonation of the Devonian in the Great Basin resulted in the recognition of three assemblage-zones (Clark and Becker, 1960). Later, Beach (1961) recognized an additional and younger Upper Devonian zone in central Utah. These four Upper Devonian zones were used along with a basal Mississippian conodont zone in defining the Devonian-Mississippian contact in central Utah (Clark and Beach, 1961). The degree of precision of this zonation compares favorably with that recently accomplished in the Upper Mississippi Valley (Collinson and others, 1962).

Study of conodonts in the Lower and Middle Devonian rocks of Utah and Nevada has shown the presence of several zones which have been compared with conodont occurrences in the Gedinnian, Siegenian, and Emsian stages of the European sequence (Clark and Ethington, 1966). The Middle Devonian of the Great Basin has yielded fewer specimens, and only a single species, *Polygnathus linguiformis* Hinde, is persistent throughout this interval.

Ziegler (1962b) reported the presence of ten conodont assemblages divisible into 24 subzones for which he proposed zonation in the Upper Devonian of Germany. Identification of many of these zones has been subsequently reported from Iowa (Klapper and Furnish, 1963; Anderson, 1966), Alberta (Clark and Ethington, 1965); Montana, Wyoming, and South Dakota (Klapper, 1966), and from Western Australia (Glenister and Klapper, 1966).

A review of Upper Devonian conodonts has been attempted with the idea of comparing the German system of zonation with that in the Great Basin. In addition, material has been secured from Upper Devonian stratigraphic levels not previously studied in the Great Basin. This review has led to the recognition of 12 distinct conodont assemblages in the Great Basin Upper Devonian, each of which corresponds in sequence and important faunal elements to the zones defined in the Upper Devonian of Germany (Ziegler, 1962b). With the multiple zonation now recognized in the Lower and Middle Devonian of the Great Basin (Clark and Ethington, 1966), a useful Devonian zonation with conodonts is available.

The primary task of conodont students until now has been the recording of basic taxonomic and stratigraphic data. This report, as such, is primarily a biostratigraphic study of Great Basin Devonian rocks. Although much work of this nature remains to be done, it is already time that the serious student can look beyond this initial kind of work to the equally valuable and perhaps more interesting biologic and ecologic research. In general, the material secured for this study is not of sufficient quantity or quality to permit biometric analysis, nor has it been possible to enlarge upon the poorly understood concept of multi-element biologic species or of evolution in conodonts. However, the taxonomy and stratigraphy reported here become part of a larger body of information published during the last few years which will form the basis of the varied biologic as well as paleoecologic and paleobiogeographic determinations. These latter studies offer more of a challenge than similar studies of any other fossil group.

# STRATIGRAPHY

## GENERAL STATEMENT

The Upper Devonian rocks of the Great Basin consist of thick sequences of lime-stones and shales in the eastern (miogeosynclinal) part and these same lithologies plus highly siliceous types in the western (eugeosynclinal) part. The formations in which conodonts are known to occur in this area include several unnamed forma-tions of western facies rocks which have been thrust into contact with eastern facies rocks in north-central Nevada. Roberts and others (1958) have given some of the details of stratigraphy and structure in this area.

## LOCALITIES

Figure 1 shows the general geographic area in which individual sections were studied. Figures 2–8 show localities for each section referred to in the text. Sev-eral sections are located in areas for which map coverage is limited to the 1:250,000 map series. Section, township, and range are indicated where surveying is complete.

In the Confusion Range of western Utah (Fig. 1), the Pilot Shale is well ex-posed in more or less continuous outcrops for more than 10 miles. Three sections were measured and studied in detail at points of better outcrops in the Pilot strike valley and, in addition, key beds (*e. g.*, C-19 of section C in Appendix) were traced for several miles from the measured sections along strike and samples were taken at places other than at positions above and below the key beds in measured sec-tions. These samples are located geographically with respect to the measured sec-tions under the described occurrence of each species as well as in the register of samples (Table 1). Their stratigraphic positions are plotted on the composite Pilot Shale section (Fig. 7) and on the Confusion composite section (Fig. 9). Strati-graphic positions of other samples are given in measured sections in the Appendix.

## WESTERN FACIES

The best conodont fauna obtained from western facies rocks is that found in the Mary's Mountain section in Nevada (Fig. 2). The Devonian rocks here have not been studied in detail but they are apparently on the upper plate of a thrust which has moved from the west. Measurable outcrops of this unnamed formation are lacking and no section is presented, but the abundant and well-preserved fauna is present in blocks and loose rubble scattered over several hundred feet on the moun-tain side. Carefully marked samples were taken from various levels of this loose material but all samples had the same *Polygnathus dubia* (=*asymmetrica?*)[1,2] fauna. More than 20 pounds of this bioclastic limestone with abundant rounded quartz has been processed in 1:7 acetic acid. Neither thickness of this lithology nor its

[1] If the name *Polygnathus asymmetrica* were to replace P. *dubia* Hinde, as Ziegler and others (1964) suggested, the zonal name *dubia* would also be changed to *asymmetrica*. By late 1966, no such name change had been proposed to the International Commission on Zoological Nomenclature or generally agreed to by specialists. The use of *P. asymmetrica*, therefore, is highly dubious (Glenister and Klapper, 1966), an uncertainty reflected in the designations used throughout.

[2] The International Commission on Zoological Nomenclature recently decided that the Latinized ending *gnathus* should now be treated as masculine. This affects many names (*e.g.*, *dubia* should be *dubius*) used in this report.

relationship to the other Devonian rocks of this thrusted zone has been determined, but J. Fred Smith and Keith Ketner, U. S. Geological Survey, who discovered this conodont fauna, are engaged in extensive mapping here.

A *Polygnathus dubia* (= *asymmetrica?*) fauna, like that found in the Mary's Mountain section, has been obtained from the lower part of the upper Devils Gate For-

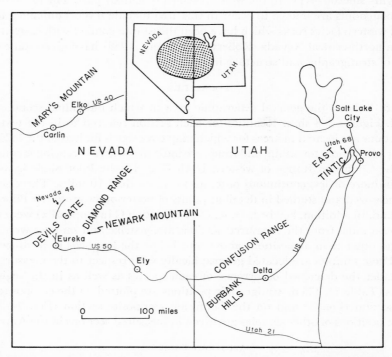

Figure 1.   General area of occurrences of Upper Devonian formations studied in the Great Basin

mation at Devils Gate Pass, Nevada (*see* Fig. 3; section in Appendix). Here it is in sequence with younger Upper Devonian zones and probably illustrates the same relationships with younger Upper Devonian rocks as will eventually be determined for the Mary's Mountain section. The fauna of Mary's Mountain is much better preserved and more diversified and constitutes about a third of the fauna studied.

Upper Devonian conodonts from unnamed formations below and above the thrust planes in the Independence Mountains and adjacent ranges of the Carlin, Nevada, area have been identified by the writers, but only the Mary's Mountain material is included as part of this report.

### EASTERN FACIES

*Introductory Statement.*   The eastern Nevada-western Utah Upper Devonian (miogeosyncline facies) includes the upper part of the Devils Gate Limestone, the upper Guilmette, the Pilot Shale, the Pinyon Peak Limestone, and the lower part of the Fitchville Formation.

*Devils Gate Limestone.* This formation was named for exposures at Devils Gate Pass, about 8 miles northwest of Eureka, Nevada, along U.S. Highway 50 (Merriam, 1940, p. 16; *see also* Fig. 3 and detailed section in Appendix). Only the upper

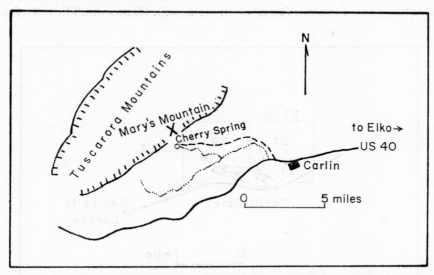

Figure 2. Unnamed Upper Devonian formation at Mary's Mountain, Nevada. Occurrence is on small hill above and north of Cherry Springs, northwest of Carlin. Base *from* Winnemucca, Nevada, sheet (NK11–11), Army Map Service, 1:250,000 series

part of the formation is exposed, but all the formation dated as Late Devonian is present. It was defined as the upper part of the Nevada Limestone of Hague (1892), and when Merriam (1963, p. 50) defined the formation in 1940, "emphasis was placed on paleontologic criteria . . . subsequent work . . . has demonstrated mappability. . . ." The formation consists of 2000 feet of dark-gray and black, thick-bedded limestone with interbedded calcareous shales. Merriam (1963, p. 54–56) discussed the megafauna of the Devils Gate with emphasis on the brachiopods and corals. He concluded (p. 54) that the Devils Gate Limestone includes "late Devonian and probable late Middle Devonian" rock.

Studies were made at the type section in Devils Gate Pass where the Upper Devonian part is approximately 1000 feet thick, in the northern Diamond Mountains, and in the southern Diamond Mountains area on Newark Mountain. These sections are all near Eureka, Nevada. The best microfossils were obtained in Devils Gate Pass where *Manticoceras* was found with the *Polygnathus dubia* (= *asymmetrica?*) fauna. Younger *Ancyrognathus triangularis* and *Palmatolepis triangularis* faunas are present as well (Fig. 3). The youngest fauna of the Devils Gate (*rhomboidea* zone) was recognized only in the northern Diamond Mountains (Fig. 4).

*Guilmette Formation.* The eastern equivalent, in part, of the Devils Gate Formation is the Guilmette Formation, several thousand feet of carbonate and argillaceous rock. This formation was studied by Nolan (1935, p. 20–21) in the Gold

Hill area of Utah and has long been recognized to contain fossils of Middle Devonian age. Species of the basal Upper Devonian ammonoid *Manticoceras* occur in the uppermost beds of the Guilmette Formation in the Confusion Range of western Utah (Fig. 5). The uppermost few hundred feet have also yielded a good *Ancyrognathus triangularis* conodont fauna which occurs with *Manticoceras*. The microfauna

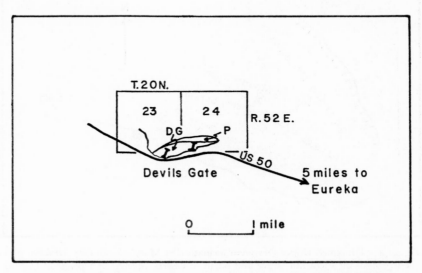

Figure 3.  Locality of Devils Gate Formation (section F) in Devils Gate Pass, Nevada. DG, Devils Gate Formation; P, Pilot Shale. *See* Appendix for further explanation. Line of section on left is lower part of upper Devils Gate, and on right is upper part of upper Devils Gate. Base *from* Whistler Mountain, Nevada, quadrangle, 15-minute topographic series, U. S. Geological Survey

was described by John Chapman in 1958 (M. S. thesis, Univ. of Kansas). Poorly preserved specimens identified tentatively as *Palmatolepis subrecta* have been found several hundred feet below the upper beds of the Guilmette. Because the upper beds are considered to belong to the *Ancyrognathus triangularis* zone and because *Palmatolepis subrecta* is known to range at least one subzone lower (the lowest major zone of the Upper Devonian), it is apparent that the Middle to Upper Devonian contact is at least two hundred feet below the top of the Guilmette Formation.

*Pilot Shale.*  The type section of the Pilot is on Pilot Knob near Ely, Nevada. The Pilot is equivalent to the lowest beds of the White Pine Shale of Hague (1892, p. 65). Spencer (1917, p. 24) first defined the Pilot Shale, and Nolan and others (1956, p. 52) reported that the thickness of the formation ranges from 315 to 1000 feet in the eastern Great Basin. The formation consists of black siliceous shales interbedded with arenaceous limestones at the base; the shales are the dominant lithology in the upper part of the section. The conodont faunas obtained by most workers have been from the arenaceous limestones; one of the best layers occurs about 50 feet above the last massive limestones of the Guilmette Formation (Fig. 5).

The fauna persists for many miles along the strike of the bed. Samples of this rock treated with acetic acid yielded primarily rounded quartz grains and conodonts.

Nolan and others (1956, p. 53) suggested that the upper part of the Pilot may be Early Mississippian and, although this idea has been followed by some students working in this area, conclusive evidence for such an age assignment has not been

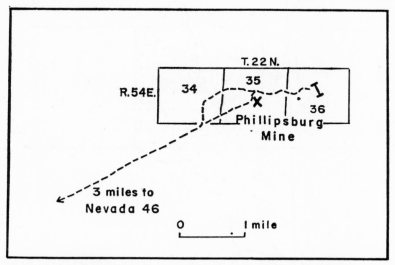

Figure 4.   Locality of Devils Gate Formation in northern Diamond Mountains, Nevada. Section is about 20 miles north of Eureka, Nevada. Upper bed of Devils Gate below Pilot Shale is sample E-1 (X), *see* Table 2. Base *from* Eureka, Nevada, quadrangle, 15-minute series, U. S. Geological Survey

published. For example, Hose (1966) concluded that the upper Pilot is Kinder-hookian because its invertebrate fauna resembles that of the Louisiana Limestone of east-central Missouri. Although all the difficulties with the age of the Louisiana Limestone may not have been solved, the best recent work[3] suggests that a Mississippian age for the Louisiana is untenable (Collinson, 1961; Scott and Collinson, 1961). Langenheim (1960) summarized other problems concerning the age of the upper Pilot beds. Shale samples could not be thoroughly disaggregated for this study because of the siliceous nature of the cement. Bedding surfaces were examined with the microscope in an attempt to find recognizable microfaunas, but this too was unsuccessful. The youngest Upper Devonian conodonts obtained in the Pilot are here interpreted as representing the lower part of the *quadrantinodosa* (*Platyclymenia*) zone in Germany. At the section in the Burbank Hills of western Utah this occurrence is about 250 feet below the lithologic contact of the Pilot Shale and the Joana Limestone. The lower 10 feet of the Joana Limestone in Tollhouse Canyon of the southern Diamond Mountains has yielded a good *Siphonodella* fauna, the same as that which Collinson and others (1962) consider

[3] Later megafauna evidence (Gutshick and Rodriguez, 1967), which shows that the Louisiana Limestone may be Mississippian, may affect the age of the upper Pilot.

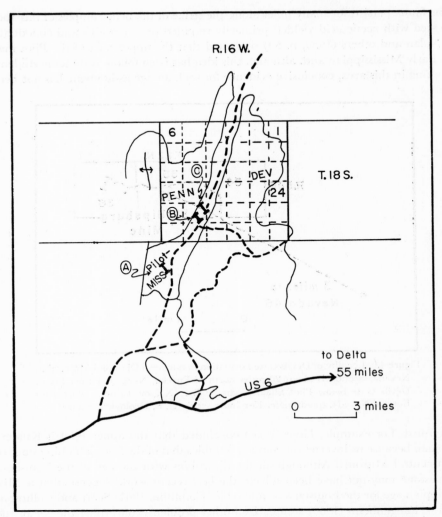

Figure 5.   Locality of Pilot Shale sections in Confusion Range, western Utah. *See* Appendix for explanation of sections A, B, and C. Dashed section-lines not surveyed. Base *from* Hintze, 1960a. Guilmette section at base of section B, sections 32 and 33

Kinderhookian in age but not the earliest part of the Kinderhookian. There are several hundred feet of post-lower *quadrantinodosa* and pre-lower Kinderhookian rocks which cannot be correlated on the basis of conodonts. Unfortunately, this interval includes the important Devonian-Mississippian time transition. Also, structural complications in the critical part of the section at most outcrops make this problem difficult.

The Pilot Shale was sampled at localities in the Confusion Range (Fig. 5) and in the Burbank Hills of western Utah (Fig. 6), in the A–1 Canyon area north of

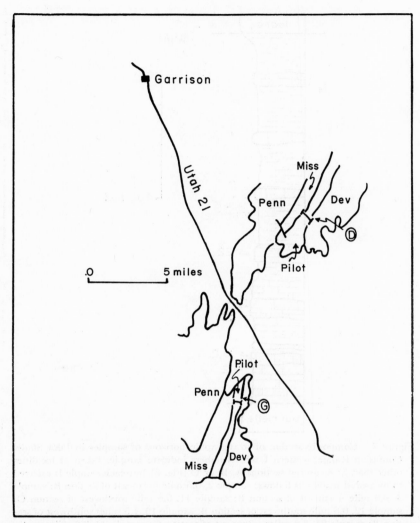

Figure 6.   Locality of Pilot Shale sections in the Burbank Hills, western Utah.
Section G (Appendix), south of Utah 21 and section D, north of Utah 21. Base
*from* Hintze, 1960b

Wendover, Nevada, and at Devils Gate Pass, and in the southern and northern
Diamond Mountains of central Nevada. The only microfauna of note found was
in the Confusion Range and Burbank outcrops. There is a continuous exposure of
Pilot Shale, just east of Conger Springs in the Confusion Range, which extends for
more than 8 miles as a strike valley between the massive Guilmette and the Joana.
Faulting is evident but outcrops in this valley have been the most productive.
Samples from determined stratigraphic intervals but not in measured sections are
located as shown in Figure 7.

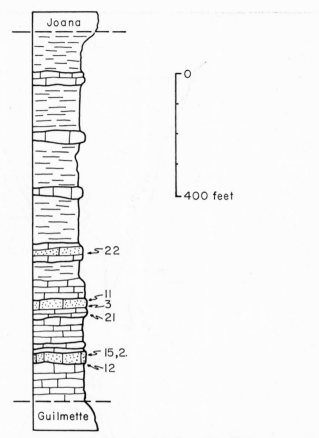

Figure 7.   Composite section of stratigraphic horizons of samples in Pilot Shale,
Confusion Range, western Utah. Numbers indicate samples taken at localities
other than at measured sections A, B, or C (Fig. 5) but each sample is referred
to measured section as follows: sample 2, 0.5 mile northeast of section B; sample
3. 0.8 mile northeast of section B; sample 11, 0.6 mile southwest of section C;
sample 12, 0.6 mile southwest of section B; sample 15, 1.5 miles southwest of section B; sample 21, 3.5 miles southwest of section C; sample 22, 3.8 miles southwest of section C. Key beds followed along strike allowed stratigraphic determination. Shale, limestone, and sandy limestone indicated; *see also* Table 2.

*Pinyon Peak Limestone and Fitchville Formation.*  The Pinyon Peak Limestone was
recognized by Lindgren and Loughlin (1919, p. 36) as a distinctive unit in the
Tintic district of west-central Utah (Fig. 8). This formation has been mapped by
Morris (1957) and Morris and Lovering (1961) who have considered it to include
Late Devonian and Early Mississippian rocks. The Fitchville Formation was described by Morris and Lovering (1961, p. 82) and considered to be Mississippian
throughout. Rigby and Clark (1962, p. 23) have summarized the sedimentological

as well as the paleontological aspects of Late Devonian and Early Mississippian
history in central Utah:

"(1) coarse clastics deposited as the result of local uplifts, referred to as the Stansbury and
Victoria Formations; (2) fine clastics and argillaceous carbonates deposited over the coarser
clastic units and peripheral to the much reduced uplifts, referred to as the Pinyon Peak Limestone; (3) relatively pure carbonate deposits, of the Fitchville Formation, gradational from the
underlying argillaceous limestone sequence. These three facies are not time restricted, but grade
laterally and vertically into one another."

No Mississippian conodonts were found in the Pinyon Peak, but representatives of part of the *velifera* or late Upper Devonian were found in the middle of

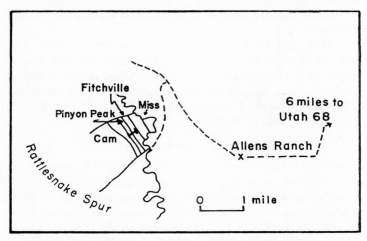

Figure 8.  Locality of Pinyon Peak and Fitchville formations (section
RS) on Rattlesnake Spur in East Tintic area, central Utah. Base *from*
Morris and Lovering (1961, Pl. 2)

the section on Rattlesnake Spur of central Utah (Fig. 8). In addition, conodonts
interpreted as representing the *costatus* or youngest Upper Devonian conodont
zone in Germany have been obtained in the overlying Fitchville Formation on
Rattlesnake Spur. It would appear that the Pinyon Peak as well as the lower part
of the overlying Fitchville Formation is Upper Devonian (Beach, 1961; Clark and
Beach, 1961; Rigby and Clark, 1962). Morris and Lovering (1961, p. 77) report
three groups of Late Devonian megafossils from the Pinyon Peak Formation but
include the discussion of this formation under a Devonian-Mississippian heading.
The microfauna in and stratigraphically above this formation suggests that it is
completely Late Devonian. In the discussion of the Fitchville Formation Morris
and Lovering (1961, p. 85–87) indicate that fossils have been collected from nearly
every lithologic unit of the formation and that all the fossils are Early Mississippian.
The only fossil collections which are correlated with a precise stratigraphic interval
are those listed (Morris and Lovering, 1961, p. 86) as coming from units 4 and 5
of their measured section. According to this section (p. 86), these two stratigraphic

units occur more than 100 feet above the base of the formation. Kinderhookian conodonts have been reported from 70 feet above the base of the section on Rattlesnake Spur in central Utah (Beach, 1961, p. 43), and work now complete (R. I. Pinney, Ph. D. thesis, Univ. of Wisconsin) indicates that Early Mississippian conodonts may occur as low as 30 feet above the base. This strengthens the contention of Clark and Beach (1961), Rigby and Clark (1962, p. 19), and this report that the Pinyon Peak and the lower beds of the Fitchville Formation in the Tintic area are most likely Late Devonian.

Nomenclature in use prior to 1961 was stabilized by Morris and Lovering (1961), who recognized two formations (Fitchville and Gardison) in the old Gardner Formation. Therefore, in Beach's (1961, p. 43) report of Devonian conodonts, the lower beds of the Gardner are equivalent to the lower beds of the Fitchville of current nomenclature.

The Pinyon Peak and overlying Fitchville Formation have been studied over much of their outcrop belt in central Utah. The most valuable microfauna has been obtained from the Rattlesnake Spur section. Good Kinderhookian microfossils as well as Early Mississippian megafossils have been reported from the lower middle and upper parts of the Fitchville (Clark, 1954, p. 25; Beach, 1961, p. 43; Morris and Lovering, 1961, p. 86–87).

SECTIONS AND SAMPLES

Measured sections for the important conodont-bearing formations are given in the Appendix. Conodonts were obtained at most localities in an average of 35 per cent of the samples taken. Where material was fragmentary or no diagnostic species was present which could be used in zonal correlation, no detailed section is presented. This includes the Devils Gate Formation in the Newark Mountain, Nevada, and east of Phillipsburg Mine in the Diamond Mountains, Nevada. At this latter locality only a single sample yielded significant results. This sample contained a fauna diagnostic of the *rhomboidea* zone and was obtained in the upper bed of the formation at the contact with the Pilot Shale (*see* Fig. 4).

Fragmentary material was also obtained from the Pilot Shale at Devils Gate Pass, in A–1 Canyon, north of Wendover, Nevada, as well as in sections figured by Clark and Becker (1960, p. 1665).

Stratigraphic positions of samples critical for this study are listed in the measured sections, and, for certain Pilot Shale samples, in Figure 7.

Approximately 2 kg of rock was taken for each sample and from 250 g to the entire sample was processed. The amount depended upon the quantity and quality of the fauna obtained. In many instances localities were revisited and additional samples taken where additional information was necessary. Technique for sample preparation is the same as that described by Clark and Becker (1960, p. 1662).

Lithologies of each sample are given in measured sections of the Appendix. Arenaceous limestones contained the best faunas but fine-grained limestones, dolomites, and calcareous sandstones also were processed with a high degree of success. The presence of conodonts in hard siliceous shale and other noncarbonate types which are not so easily disaggregated with acid has posed a major problem.

TABLE 1.   IMPORTANT SAMPLES OF UPPER DEVONIAN IN THE GREAT BASIN AND
THEIR GEOGRAPHIC AND BIOSTRATIGRAPHIC LOCATIONS

| Sample | Formation | Figure show-ing locality | Zone |
|---|---|---|---|
| 2 | Pilot | 7 | *u. gigas* |
| 3 | Pilot | 7 | *u. P. triangularis* |
| 11 | Pilot | 7 | *u. P. triangularis* |
| 12 | Pilot | 7 | *l. gigas* |
| 15 | Pilot | 7 | *u. gigas* |
| 21 | Pilot | 7 | *m. P. triangularis* |
| 22 | Pilot | 7 | *l. quadrantinodosa?* |
| A-15 | Pilot | 5 | .. |
| lower B-34 | Pilot | 5 | *l. P. triangularis* |
| B-36 | Pilot | 5 | *m.-u. P. triangularis* |
| C-12 | Pilot | 5 | *?* |
| C-19 | Pilot | 5 | *l. crepida* |
| lower G-9 | Pilot | 6 | *l. quadrantinodosa* |
| G-6 | Pilot | 6 | *?* |
| E-1 | Devils Gate | 4 | *rhomboidea* |
| F-5, 97' above base | Devils Gate | 3 | *m. P. triangularis* |
| F-6 | Devils Gate | 3 | *m. P. triangularis* |
| F-15 | Devils Gate | 3 | *A. triangularis* |
| F-16 | Devils Gate | 3 | *A. triangularis* |
| F-24 | Devils Gate | 3 | *m. P. dubia* (=*asymmetrica?*) |
| F-26 | Devils Gate | 3 | *m. P. dubia* (=*asymmetrica?*) |
| RS-5, 6 | Pinyon Peak | 8 | *velifera* |
| RS-20 | Fitchville | 8 | *m. costatus* |
| M. M.* | U. Devonian | 2 | *m. P. dubia* (=*asymmetrica?*) |
| Gu | Guilmette | 7 | *A. triangularis* |

* Mary's Mountain

Table 1 lists the most important samples obtained for this study and their geo-graphic positions as well as important stratigraphic data.

# BIOSTRATIGRAPHY

## GENERAL STATEMENT

The zones utilized by Clark and Becker (1960) in their work with the Upper Devonian rocks of the eastern Great Basin included Zone A, considered of late *Manticoceras* (*to* I) age of the European standard; Zone B, late *Manticoceras* to early *Cheiloceras;* and Zone C, late *Cheiloceras* or early *Platyclymenia* (*to* II–*to* III). Beach (1961) recognized what he determined to be Zone C in the Pinyon Peak Limestone of central Utah and proposed a Zone D for rocks of possible *Oxyclymenia-Wocklumeria* (*to* IV–*to* VI) age in the Pinyon Peak-Fitchville section of central Utah.

The current study has led to the recognition of more detailed zonation for the Upper Devonian rocks previously studied, and the originally defined zones are now further differentiated. The *P. dubia* (=*asymmetrica?*) zone has not previously been recognized in the Great Basin. Five distinct assemblages can now be defined within what was originally included in the "Zone A." Likewise, two distinct assemblage-zones can be recognized within the original "Zone B." The "Zone C" of Clark and Becker (1960) can be differentiated into two parts, and the "Zone C" of Beach (1961) and Clark and Beach (1961) is now recognized to be younger than any of the previous "Zone C" intervals. Additional finds have helped define "Zone D" of these writers as basal *Wocklumeria* (*to* VI) age and the youngest Devonian known in the Great Basin. The 12 zones thus recognized (Fig. 9) are not designated with new names or numbers but with the terminology defined by Ziegler (1962b) for the German rocks. For general correlation the three zones of Clark and Becker (A, B, C) and the two of Beach ("C," D) give five broad intervals which may have value. Previous zonation and that described in this report are compared in Fig. 10.

## UPPER DEVONIAN ASSEMBLAGES AND ZONES

*Introductory Statement.* Figure 11 shows assemblage-zones determined by Ziegler (1962b). Correlation with Great Basin stratigraphic units is also indicated. It is of particular significance to note that although the complete sequence of zones has not been determined anywhere else in the world, the same general arrangement of many of the zones is now known in central United States (Klapper and Furnish, 1963; Anderson, 1966), western Canada (Clark and Ethington, 1965), Western Australia (Glenister and Klapper, 1966), as well as different parts of Europe (*e. g.*, Spassov, 1965, for Bulgaria, and Bouckaert and Ziegler, 1965, for Belgium).

*Germany.* The German Upper Devonian has previously been divided on the basis of characteristic ammonoid occurrences (Fig. 11). Also, the traditional map designation for the Devonian System in Germany has been the letter *t*. In this way *tu* has been used to characterize the Lower Devonian, *tm*, the Middle, and *to*, the Upper. These trisubsystems have been divided into major divisions of *to* I, II, III, *etc.*, which in turn have been subdivided into *to* I*α*, *β*, *etc.* The known distribution of conodonts led to a refinement of the subdivisions; *e.g.*, *to* II*α* can be subdivided into a "mittlere *crepida* zone" and an "obere *crepida* zone," each with its own assemblage of conodonts.

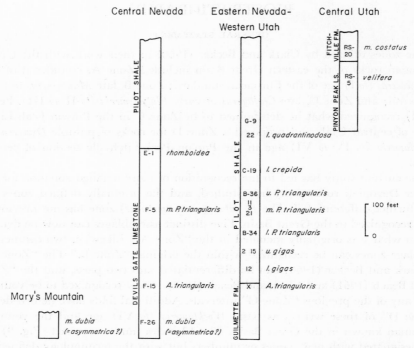

Figure 9.   Upper Devonian sections in the Great Basin showing composite sample
data and comparison of zones recognized in the formations. Sample symbols
refer to sample register (Table 1).

The distinctiveness of many of the 24 conodont assemblages which Ziegler has
recognized is based on first and last occurrences of species. The concept of first
and last occurrence has been criticized (e.g., Kay, 1947), but Ziegler (1962b) has
confirmed these occurrences in a number of widely separated German sections. In
addition, many diagnostic species in Ziegler's assemblages appear to be true phylo-
genetic sequences (ancestors and descendants) whose life spans have clearly been
recorded (see Ziegler, 1962b, Figs. 3, 4, 12, etc.). Müller (1956a, p. 1334–1337) and
others have emphasized the ubiquitous occurrence of conodonts in many parts of
the world, and the occurrence of the same sequences of conodonts in western North
America adds further support to the validity of these ideas.

Great Basin.   All the zones described here are not found in a single section in
the Great Basin. The best oldest Upper Devonian assemblage found is in the
western facies rocks where younger assemblages are poorly known. Likewise, the
youngest Upper Devonian assemblage found occurs in the Fitchville Formation of
central Utah and has not been recognized elsewhere. The Pilot Shale of western
Utah contains representatives of five of the ten major conodont zones, and the
sections in the Confusion Range have been most productive.

Table 2 lists the fauna of each conodont zone in the Great Basin. It should be
pointed out that the writers consider any difference between the Upper Devonian

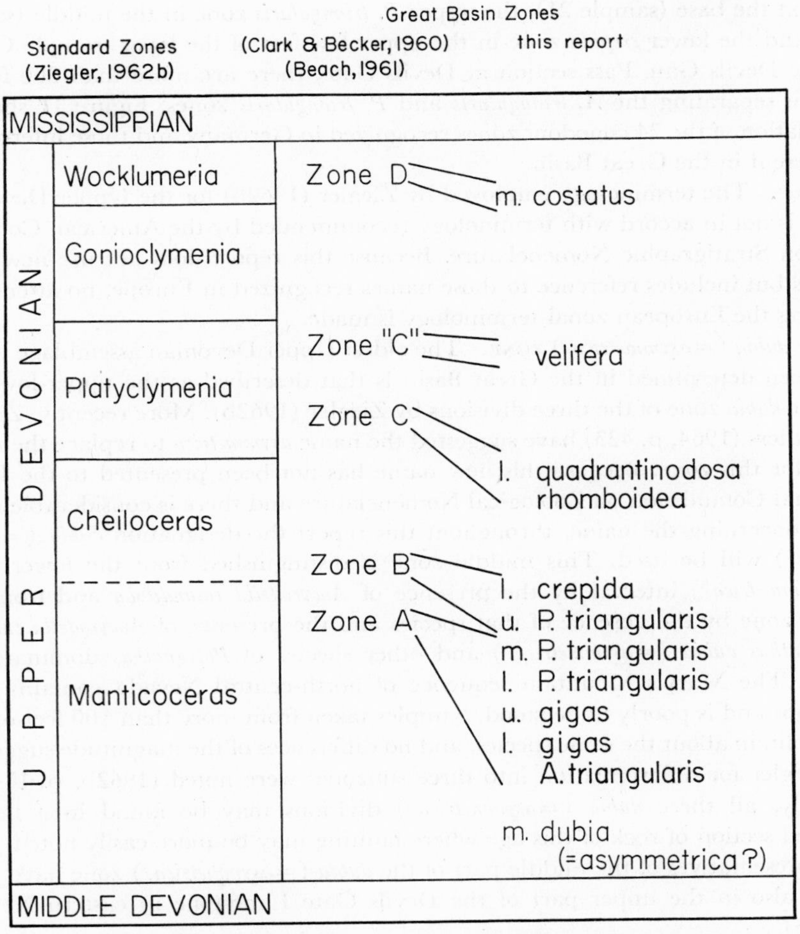

Figure 10.  Standard ammonoid zones of the Upper Devonian of Germany compared with correlations of Clark and Becker (1960) and Beach (1961) and with zones of this report

zones described in Europe and those of the Great Basin of minor nature. Each of the European zones correlated with similar intervals in the Great Basin, as well as the Great Basin equivalents, is characterized by one or more species not reported in adjacent intervals or by the absence of species which are known to be important constituents of other zones. Hence, the minor differences in ranges of certain species do not seem significant when their total range is compared to the important species of a particular zone and it is assumed that the ranges of the important species are the same on both continents. Further, it should be pointed out that distribution of the different conodont zones in the Great Basin rocks is not uniform. In the Pilot Shale sections of the Confusion Range, one thick arenaceous limestone carries three of the zones Ziegler has recognized in Germany—the middle *P. triangularis* zone at the base (sample 21), the upper *P. triangularis* zone in the middle (sample 11), and the lower *crepida* zone in the upper few feet of the layer (sample C–19). In the Devils Gate Pass section at Devils Gate, there are more than 200 feet of section separating the *A. triangularis* and *P. triangularis* zones. Figure 11 shows a correlation of the 24 conodont zones recognized in Germany and those interpreted as present in the Great Basin.

*Zones.* The terminology employed by Ziegler (1962b) for the Upper Devonian zones is not in accord with terminology recommended by the American Commission on Stratigraphic Nomenclature. Because this report does not use new zone names but includes reference to those names recognized in Europe, no attempt at revising the European zonal terminology is made.

THE *dubia* ( = *asymmetrica?*) ZONE. The oldest Upper Devonian assemblage which has been determined in the Great Basin is that described as the upper-lower or middle *dubia* zone of the three divisions by Ziegler (1962b). More recently, Ziegler and others (1964, p. 423) have suggested the name *asymmetrica* to replace the name *dubia* for this zone. Because this new name has not been presented to the International Commission on Zoological Nomenclature and there is considerable question concerning the name, throughout this report the designation *dubia* ( = *asymmetrica?*) will be used. This middle zone is distinguished from the lower *dubia* ( = *asymmetrica?*) interval by the presence of *Ancyrodella rotundiloba* and from the upper zone by the absence of that species and the presence of *Ancyrodella curvata*. *Polygnathus dubia* ( = *asymmetrica?*) and other species of *Polygnathus* dominate the fauna. The Mary's Mountain sequence of north-central Nevada contains poor outcrops and is poorly understood. Samples taken from more than 100 feet of section contain about the same species, and no differences of the magnitude suggested by Ziegler for differentiation into three subzones were noted (1962b, p. 17–20). Possibly, all three *dubia* ( = *asymmetrica?*) divisions may be found in a better-exposed section of rock of this age where faulting may be more easily noted.

Representatives of the middle part of the *dubia* ( = *asymmetrica?*) zone have been found also in the upper part of the Devils Gate Limestone in eastern Nevada (Fig. 3).

This zone belongs to the *Pharciceras*-schichten (*to* Iα) of the lower *Manticoceras* interval of the German standard (Ziegler, 1962b).

THE *Ancyrognathus triangularis* ZONE: This second major zone of Ziegler (1962b) and the fourth in his ascending sequence is developed in the upper Guilmette and lowest Pilot Shale of western Utah and in the Devils Gate Limestone of eastern Nevada where it occurs with species of the ammonoid *Manticoceras*. The assemblage of this zone is characterized by the name species of the zone as well as abundant *Palmatolepis foliacea* and *P. subrecta*. According to Ziegler (1962b, p. 20), the occurrence of at least *P. foliacea* indicates the upper part of the *Ancyrognathus triangularis* zone. Most species of this zone in the Great Basin (*see* Table 1) are also present in the overlying *gigas* zone. Identification of this zone in this area is based on its stratigraphic position below a definite *gigas* zone assemblage and the absence of species which are present in the *gigas* zone of Europe and the Great Basin, *e.g.*, *Ancyrodella buckeyensis*, *Palmatolepis unicornis*.

GERMAN CONODONT ZONES    GREAT BASIN

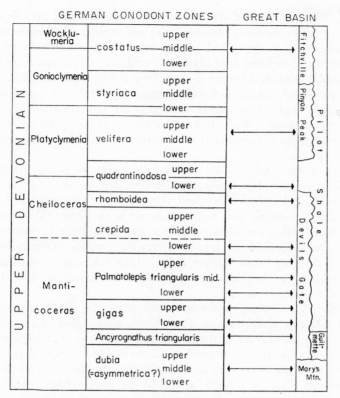

Figure 11. Correlation and classification of Great Basin conodont zones with those recognized in Germany

This assemblage is best developed in the upper beds of the Guilmette Formation of the Confusion Range in western Utah and was described by John Chapman (1958, M. S. thesis, Univ. of Kansas). This writer described more than 30 species at least some of which were obtained from intervals above the Guilmette. The assemblage is also well represented in the Devils Gate Pass, Nevada, which is in the upper part of the Devils Gate Limestone (sample F–15). The assemblage belongs to the middle part of the middle *Manticoceras* interval (*to* Iγ).

THE *gigas* ZONE: The *gigas* zone was named *Palmatolepis rhenana* by Ziegler (1962b), but recently Klapper and Furnish (1963, p. 406–407) have indicated that *P. rhenana* is a junior synonym of *P. gigas* and so renamed the *rhenana* zone the *gigas* zone. The lower *gigas* assemblage includes *Palmatolepis subrecta*, *P. unicornis*, and species of *Ancyrodella* and *Polygnathus*. The assemblage is present in the lower Pilot Shale of the Confusion Range of western Utah and is considered to represent the upper part of the middle *Manticoceras* interval (highest *to* Iγ).

The upper *gigas* zone includes by definition the interval after the last occurrence of *Palmatolepis foliacea* and where *Ancyrognathus asymmetrica* begins. The name species is abundant in this interval in the Great Basin.

Ziegler (1962b) questioned the "Zone A" fauna of Clark and Becker (1960) because these latter students indicated the occurrence of *Palmatolepis marginata* (=*P. delicatula*) with *P. linguiformis* in that zone. Ziegler was correct in questioning this occurrence because re-study of the original sample material has proved that the samples with *P. delicatula* are not from the same strata as *P. linguiformis*. This latter species is known only from the upper part of the *gigas* zone in Germany and is assumed to indicate the same interval in the Great Basin.

The upper *gigas* zone is equivalent to the middle of the upper *Manticoceras* zone (*to* Iδ). It is widespread in the lower Pilot Shale of the Confusion Range of western Utah.

THE *Palmatolepis triangularis* ZONE: This zone comprises three subzones: lower, middle, and upper. The lower *triangularis* zone is distinguished by the presence of the name species, *Palmatolepis triangularis*, prior to the first occurrence of *P. delicatula delicatula* and *P. delicatula clarki*. A single sample in the lower Pilot Shale (base of sample B–34) contains the fauna of this assemblage. Perhaps more convincing than this meager fossil evidence is the stratigraphic position of the fauna of sample B–34, almost 200 feet below sample B–26, which contains a good fauna and is considered middle *P. triangularis* age. Therefore, fauna and stratigraphic position are used in defining this zone.

The middle *P. triangularis* zone is characterized by the first appearance of *Palmatolepis delicatula delicatula* and *P. delicatula clarki*, plus other characteristic species (*see* Table 1). This interval plus the preceding four (*A. triangularis*–lower *P. triangularis*) were collectively grouped as "Zone A" in Clark and Becker (1960). Fauna of this zone has been recognized in the upper beds of the Devils Gate Formation at Devils Gate Pass, Nevada, and in the lower-middle part of the Pilot Shale in the Confusion Range of western Utah.

The upper *P. triangularis* zone assemblage is well developed in the lower-middle and middle Pilot Shale of western Utah and is characterized by the first occurrence of *Palmatolepis tenuipunctata*. *P. delicatula clarki* (=*P. marginata* var. B of Clark and Becker), *P. subperlobata*, *P. quadrantinodosalobata*, and the name species of this zone are common elements of this fauna. This includes the first assemblage included in "Zone B" of Clark and Becker (1960) and, as pointed out then and later confirmed by Ziegler (1962b), it is in the "Grenzbereich" or transition area of the *Manticoceras* and *Cheiloceras* intervals.

THE *crepida* ZONE: Ziegler (1962b) recognized three divisions of this zone in Germany: a lower, distinguished by the presence of *Palmatolepis crepida* before the occurrence of *P. termini;* a middle zone, characterized by the presence of these two species; and an upper, which is characterized by the name species and *P. glabra glabra*.

The lower of these three zones is well developed in the middle Pilot Shale of western Utah and was included in "Zone B" of Clark and Becker (1960). This is considered to represent the *to* IIα interval of the *Cheiloceras* zone in Germany.

The fauna here considered to represent the lower part of the *crepida* zone contains all the important elements of this zone reported in Europe (Ziegler, 1962b, p. 28, Tables 2, 3) except for the name species, *Palmatolepis crepida*. The recognition of this zone depends upon the acceptance of the first occurrence of typical *P. quadrantinodosalobata* (Ziegler, 1962b, p. 28, 73) with *P. subperlobata* and *P. minuta minuta* (Tables 2 and 5 of Ziegler, 1962b) as indicating the lower part of the zone even in the absence of *P. crepida*. Ziegler's Table 3 (1962b) indicates the occurrence of *P. quadrantinodosalobata* in the Sessacker-Schurf I in the *P. triangularis* zone, but the absence of this species at this horizon on his other tables (*e.g.*, Tables 2 and 4) and his remarks (p. 28 and 73) concerning the development of two types of *P. quadrantinodosalobata* in the *P. triangularis* and *crepida* zones, respectively, would indicate that distribution of the species in this zone and below is not evidence for rejecting the distinction of either of the zones.

THE *rhomboidea* ZONE: In the northern Diamond Mountains, the uppermost beds of the Devils Gate Formation contain a rich *Palmatolepis* fauna including species which are not reported to occur together by Ziegler in Europe (1962b, p. 30–31, Tables 2, 4). *Palmatolepis crepida* and *Palmatolepis subperlobata* are present together in the Diamond Mountains Devils Gate (*see* Table 2) and in Europe occur in the *crepida* zone but no higher. These two species occur together with *P. quadrantinodosa quadrantinodosa* and *Polygnathus nodocostata*, which are reported only from the *rhomboidea* zone or higher in Europe. In addition, the fauna from the same sample contains *Palmatolepis glabra glabra*, *P. glabra pectinata*, *P. n. sub. A. Ziegler*, and *P. minuta* which are recognized in Europe as ranging below, in, and above the *rhomboidea* zone. The anomalous occurrence is completed with the occurrence of *P. glabra elongata* in the Nevada material, a species which Ziegler (1962b, p. 59, Tables 2, 4) has reported occurring first in the lower *quadrantinodosa* zone. In summary, this Devils Gate fauna contains two species reported in Europe from the *rhomboidea* zone or higher; four which range below, in, and above the *rhomboidea* zone; one species reported from the overlying *quadrantinodosa* zone only; and two species which range up to, but not in, the *rhomboidea* zone. The majority of the species would suggest the *rhomboidea* zone or higher of the European zonation and, if *P. subperlobata* and *P. crepida* were not present, the occurrence of *P. glabra elongata* in this fauna would argue for a minimum of lower *quadrantinodosa* age. The identification of the two older age species may be open to question. Ziegler (1962b, p. 30) has confirmed the identification of the *P. crepida* specimen of the sample (=*P. n. sp. aff. crepida*, Clark and Becker, 1960, p. 1671). However, the specimens referred to *P. subperlobata* from this fauna show marked differences when compared to the *P. subperlobata* from lower horizons.

The presence of three species (*Polygnathus nodocostata*, *Palmatolepis quadrantinodosa quadrantinodosa*, and *P. glabra elongata*) is considered by the writers to indicate a *rhomboidea* zone age for the fauna.

It should be pointed out that this is the most striking example of species in the Great Basin material whose ranges are evidently different from those reported in Europe. Some reworking may be possible. Also, the differences are of quite small magnitude if this report is considered simply to extend the range of two species of *Palmatolepis* into the next higher zone (upper *crepida* to *rhomboidea*) and one species of *Palmatolepis* into the next lower zone (from lower *quadrantinodosa* to *rhomboidea*). This would seem more in line with the fact that most conodonts appear to have similar ranges on a world-wide basis (*e.g.*, Ziegler, 1962b) than would develop if the entire Devils Gate assemblage were considered upper *crepida* and the range of *P. glabra elongata* extended down two zones (*rhomboidea* and *crepida*).

The *rhomboidea* fauna in Europe represents the lower part of the upper *Cheiloceras* (*to* IIβ) interval. This fauna in Nevada was designated "Zone C" of Clark and Becker (1960, p. 1666).

THE *quadrantinodosa* ZONE: In Germany, Ziegler (1962b, p. 31) defined this zone as encompassing the range of *P. quadrantinodosa marginifera* and divided it into a lower and an upper *quadrantinodosa* zone on the basis of the range of *P. quadrantinodosa inflexa*. This latter subspecies has been reported in Europe only in the lower zone.

Several *P. quadrantinodosa marginifera* and *P. quadrantinodosa inflexa* were obtained together with a few blade-type conodonts from a sample in the middle of the Pilot Shale in the Burbank Hills of westernmost Utah. If the range of *P. m. inflexa* reported in Europe is considered valid for the Utah specimens, the fauna represents the lower *quadrantinodosa* zone. Ziegler (1962b, p. 18) has indicated that this zone represents the highest part of the *Cheiloceras* beds (*to* IIβ) of the European standard. A single sample (22) from about 100 feet above the lower *crepida* interval in the vicinity of section C (Confusion Range) contains species of *P. perlobata schindewolfi* which might belong in this zone (*see* discussion under this species).

THE *velifera* ZONE: Specimens described by Beach (1961) from unit RS-5 included *Palmatolepis rugosa trachytera*. Additional specimens have been found in RS-6–12. This occurrence is in the middle part of the Pinyon Peak Limestone in central Utah. The assemblage was considered by Beach (1961, p. 41, 43) and Clark and Beach (1961, p. 150) to belong to "Zone C" of Clark and Becker (1960), but Ziegler (1962b, p. 79) has indicated that this *Palmatolepis* species ranges from the middle to the upper *velifera* zone in Germany. If this range is considered valid for the Devonian of the Great Basin, it indicates that "Zone C" of Beach (1961) is in reality younger than "Zone C" of Clark and Becker (1960). As indicated in this report, the "Zone C" of Clark and Becker (1960) is now recognized to include *rhomboidea* zone equivalent material in the Devils Gate of Nevada and lower *quadrantinodosa* zone material in the upper Pilot Shale of western Utah.

Only *P. rugosa trachytera* appears to carry much age significance in the Pinyon Peak material and the other species of *Polygnathus* do not seem diagnostic. It ranges through 50 feet in the Pinyon Peak on Rattlesnake Spur. If the range of this species in Utah is accepted as being the same as the range in Europe, it would indicate that this assemblage belongs to the middle or upper *velifera* zone or to the *to* IIIβ or *to* IV part of the *Platyclymenia* interval of the European standard.

THE *styriaca* ZONE: Conodonts representative of this zone in Europe have not yet been reported in the Devonian of the Great Basin. The rocks of the interval in which fauna of this zone would be expected have been most unproductive of fossils of any kind in the Utah-Nevada area.

THE *costatus* ZONE: The youngest of the Upper Devonian conodont zones has been recognized in the lower part of the Fitchville Formation of central Utah. This interval was designated "Zone D" by Beach (1961, p. 43) and Clark and

Beach (1961, p. 150) and was reported to be characterized by *Polygnathus styriaca*. This species has recently been redefined as *P. vogesi* (Ziegler, 1962b, p. 94) and additional material from this stratigraphic interval has yielded the important *Spathognathodus aculeatus*.

*P. vogesi* has been reported from the middle *costatus* zone through the lower Carboniferous in Europe, but *Spathognathodus aculeatus* is known only from the middle part of the lower *costatus* through the middle *costatus* zones in Europe (Ziegler, 1962b, p. 106) and in the *S. aculeatus* assemblage zone in this country (Collinson and others, 1962, p. 18). The interval represented by the occurrence of these two species together would be middle *costatus*, according to the recorded range in Europe. This is representative of the upper *Gonioclymenia* (*Wocklumeria* to VI) of the European standard and is the youngest Upper Devonian known in the Great Basin.

## SUMMARY

The preliminary conodont work in the Great Basin Devonian has been successful in the determination of multiple zones. Four Lower Devonian zones and a single Middle Devonian zone have been recognized (Clark and Ethington, 1966). Twelve Upper Devonian zones, classified against a more complete sequence in Germany, are described herein.

# SYSTEMATIC PALEONTOLOGY

## GENERAL STATEMENT

Some 96 species of 25 genera are described. Beach (1961) has described five additional Upper Devonian species from Utah: *Polygnathus nodocostata*, *P. semicostata*, *P. granulosa*, and *Hibbardella telum*, from the Pinyon Peak Limestone, and *P. styriaca* (= *P. vogesi*) from the Fitchville.

Nomenclature, in part, follows that used by Hass (1962), and reference to Fay (1952) in the synonymy is in lieu of references prior to 1949. Specimens are deposited at the U. S. National Museum (USNM), Washington, D. C., University of Wisconsin (UW), Madison, and Brigham Young University (BYU), Provo, Utah. Repository number refers to figured individual. Other specimens are in the writers' collections. Species are portrayed in Plates 1 to 9, following the bibliography.

Emended descriptions are given where other morphologic features are described or where more abundant or well-preserved material shows features that previously were poorly understood. Redescriptions are given where species have been confused and where clarification of data included in the concept is needed. New descriptions are given where previous descriptions are brief and must be expanded, although the concept is not necessarily changed because of this. Localities referred to under the heading Occurrence include sample number and relationship to reference measured section in Appendix as well as the zone to which the conodont species belongs. Geographic data include reference to the locality figure. Number of specimens per species available for this study is also indicated under Occurrence. Stratigraphic occurrence in measured sections is given in Appendix and Figure 7. Lithology of sample from which species were recovered is given in Appendix.

The diverse numbering system for samples and sections is the result of organization of samples collected by several individuals over a seven-year period.

## CONODONTS AS BIOLOGIC SPECIES

Since the beginning of serious work with conodonts, students have been aware of the possibility that an individual conodont element was only one such element of many, similar and dissimilar, of a particular biologic species. Because few complete assemblages of elements have been found together in patterns suggestive of original associations of a living animal, a terminology has developed which designates each conodont element as a species. With few exceptions, such form-species designations have not been intended to represent natural or biologic species. Just how the various form-species might be related in a single biologic species has not been determined except in the case of the few natural assemblages found.

So few natural assemblages are known that students have tried various methods of determining what constitutes a biologic species. Most promising of the recently derived methods is that of statistical association of elements plus the similarity of certain common morphologic features. This method has been used by Bergström and Sweet (1966), among others. This technique can be considered partially successful and these students grouped 70 form-species in 32 single or multi-element biologic species. There are inherent problems with such an approach, however, and such statistical associations have indicated only one type of association which may have been presented in a single biologic species. Also promising is the technique of Lindström (1964) who outlined symmetry transitions in individual elements or form-species and their possible relationship to function. A combination of techniques holds much promise.

Material of the present study is not of sufficient quantity to allow statistical determinations but certain form-species of the form-genus *Palmatolepis* give some insight. Certain specimens comprise more than 50 per cent of the fauna of many samples and such association indicates that *Palmatolepis* may have been the principal or only element of a single biologic species. How such elements would be arranged in the animal body is conjectural. Conjecture can be aided by certain observations, however. For instance, the known natural assemblages show individual elements in close proximity and in an arrangement where the denticles of each element are directly opposed to those of the paired element. Also, if Lindström's idea on conodonts serving as supports in feeding devices such as lophophores is tenable (1964), then the principal alignment of the carina-blade combination on the elements must have been arranged to catch currents and hence direct nutrients to a mouth. With these ideas in mind several possible arrangements of *Palmatolepis* have been studied, the most plausible of which is illustrated on Plate 1. Sinistral and dextral specimens or their substitutes for each of several growth stages were utilized. Although this arrangement may have little similarity to the actual one, it suggests a promising field of research on the biologic species.

Genus *Acodina* Stauffer, 1940
Type species: *A. lanceolata* Stauffer, 1940

Hass (1962, p. W43) considered *Acodina* to be a junior synonym of *Acontiodus* Pander and further indicated some question that its range is beyond the Middle Ordovician. The consistent reports of species of this genus in the Upper Devonian may indicate that this name should be retained for the post-Ordovician species.

*Acodina curvata* Stauffer
(Pl. 2, fig. 3)

*Acodina curvata* STAUFFER, 1940, Jour. Paleontology, v. 14, p. 418, Pl. 60, figs. 3, 14–16; FAY, 1952, Univ. Kansas Paleont. Contrib., Vert., art. 3, p. 60; SANNEMANN, 1955a, Senckenbergiana Lethaea, Bd. 36, p. 126, Pl. 1, fig. 17; SCHRIEL AND STOPPEL, 1960, Deutsch. Geol. Gesell. Zeit., Bd. 111, p. 672; SPASSOV, 1965, Trav. Géol. Bulgarie, sér. Paléont., v. 7, p. 82–83, Pl. 1, fig. 9

(Not *Acodina curvata* HELMS, 1959, Geologie, v. 8, no. 6, p. 663, Pl. 4, fig. 12)

REMARKS: Planoconvex cross section of the tooth and longitudinal curvature are diagnostic of this species. Details of this species are distinct from species referred to *Acontiodus* and justify the generic division.

OCCURRENCE: This species is previously known from the lower-Upper Devonian of the *Cheiloceras* zone in Europe and from Upper Devonian rocks of Minnesota. Middle *Palmatolepis triangularis* zone, Pilot Shale; sample 21 collected 3½ miles southwest of section C, Confusion Range, western Utah (Fig. 7); 6 specimens

REPOSITORY: USNM 144306

Genus *Ancyrodella* Ulrich and Bassler, 1926
Type species: *A. nodosa* Ulrich and Bassler, 1926

This Late Devonian genus is represented in the Great Basin rocks by two species. Ziegler (1962a) has traced the evolution of species of this genus in rocks of *Manticoceras* age in Europe. The trends which he demonstrated are also seen in the Great Basin rocks.

## *Ancyrodella buckeyensis* Stauffer

*Ancyrodella buckeyensis* STAUFFER, 1938, Jour. Paleonotology, v. 12, p. 418, Pl. 52, figs. 17, 18, 23, 24; FAY, 1952, Univ. Kansas Paleont. Contrib., Vert., art. 3, p. 63; MÜLLER AND MÜLLER, 1957, Jour. Paleontology, v. 31, p. 1091, Pl. 136, figs. 2, 5; FLÜGEL AND ZIEGLER, 1957, Naturw. Ver. Steiermark, Mitt., Bd. 87, Table 1; ZIEGLER, 1958, Hess. Landesamt Boden., Notizbl., Bd. 87, p. 12, 20, 28, 31, 40, Pl. 11, fig. 7; KREBS, 1959, Senckenbergiana Lethaea, Bd. 40, p. 374, 379, 380, Pl. 1, fig. 6; KREBS, 1960, Hess. Landesamt Boden., Notizbl., Bd. 88, p. 218; ZIEGLER, 1962a, Neues Jahrbuch Geol. Paläont., Abh., Bd. 114, p. 148–149, 9 figs.; ETHINGTON, 1965, Jour. Paleontology, v. 39, p. 570, Pl. 68, fig. 3
*Polygnathus rotundiloba* YOUNGQUIST, 1947, Jour. Paleontology, v. 21, p. 110, Pl. 26, fig. 6
*Polygnathus spinulosa* YOUNGQUIST, 1947, Jour. Paleontology, v. 21, p. 110, Pl. 24, fig. 9
*Ancyrodella* sp. MILLER AND YOUNGQUIST, 1947, Jour. Paleontology, v. 21, p. 503, Pl. 74, fig. 13
*Ancyrodella lobata* MILLER AND YOUNGQUIST, 1947, Jour. Paleontology, v. 21, p. 502, Pl. 74, fig. 12
*Ancyrodella nodosa* YOUNGQUIST AND MILLER, 1948, Jour. Paleontology, v. 22, p. 441, Pl. 68, figs. 13, 14

REMARKS: Ziegler (1962a) interpreted *A. buckeyensis* as a form transitional between *Ancyrodella gigas* and *A. nodosa*. This is an evolutionary sequence involving reduction of the platform. Ultimate reduction is reached in *A. ioides*.

OCCURRENCE: The species is known in the German section, in the Sweetland Creek and Independence shales of Iowa, the Olentangy Shale of Ohio, and the Martin Limestone of Arizona. Specimens in our collections are too fragmentary to figure adequately. Lower *gigas* zone, Pilot Shale; sample 12 collected 0.6 mile southwest of section B, Confusion Range, western Utah (Fig. 7); 20 specimens
REPOSITORY: USNM 144307

## *Ancyrodella rotundiloba* (Bryant)
(Pl. 2, figs. 4, 6–10, 13–15)

*Polygnathus tuberculatus* HINDE, 1879, Geol. Soc. London Quart. Jour., v. 35, p. 366, Pl. 17, fig. 10 (part); FAY, 1952, Univ. Kansas Paleont. Contrib., Vert., art. 3, p. 161
*Polygnathus rotundilobus* BRYANT, 1921, Buffalo Soc. Nat. Sci. Bull., v. 13, p. 26–27, Pl. 12, figs. 1–6, Text-fig. 7; FAY, 1952, Univ. Kansas Paleont. Contrib., Vert., art. 3, p. 159 (not YOUNGQUIST, 1947, Jour. Paleontology, v. 21, p. 110, Pl. 26, fig. 6)
*Ancyrodella rotundiloba* BRANSON AND MEHL, 1941, Denison Univ. Bull., Sci. Lab. Jour., v. 35, p. 202; BISCHOFF AND ZIEGLER, 1957, Hess. Landesamt Boden., Abh., no. 22, p. 42, Pl. 16, figs. 5–12, 14–17; ZIEGLER, 1958, Hess. Landesamt Boden., Notizbl., Bd. 87, p. 44–45, Pl. 11, figs. 11, 12a, 12b; KREBS, 1959, Senckenbergiana Lethaea, Bd. 40, p. 374, 377, Pl. 1, fig. 15; ZIEGLER, 1962a, Neues Jahrbuch Geol. Paläont., Abh., Bd. 114, p. 146–147
*Ancyrodella rotundiloba rotundiloba* GLENISTER AND KLAPPER, 1966, Jour. Paleontology, v. 40, p. 799, Pl. 85, figs. 9–13
*Ancyrodella rotundiloba alata* GLENISTER AND KLAPPER, 1966, Jour. Paleontology, v. 40, p. 799–800, Pl. 85, figs. 1–8, Pl. 86, figs. 1–4

REMARKS: During the ontogenetic development of *A. rotundiloba*, several morphologic patterns appear. These include the normal *A. rotundiloba* pattern with a more or less irregularly shaped platform, nonsymmetrical and with random node arrangement on the upper surface (figs. 9 14, 15, of Pl. 2). Another distinct type is shown on Pl. 2 (figs. 4, 7, 8, 10). On this type, the outline of platform is triangular with sharp posterior point and slight anteriorly directed lobes on either side of blade. The surface ornamentation consists of stout conical nodes which tend to become arranged in rows convergent with carina. High, narrow keels extend from the lateral corners of the pit toward the anterolateral corners but do not reach the periphery, a feature that may be somewhat different on differently sized forms. The origin of the different patterns of ornamentation can be seen in large-sized collections and it would appear that no biologic or stratigraphic difference exists among the diverse types. Müller and Clark (in press) present an expanded discussion of the ontogenetic variation of this species.

Ziegler (1962a) considered this species to have evolved from a species of *Polygnathus* such as *P. dubia* and, in turn, to be the stem from which all the other ancyrodellid species evolved. The outline of the platform is variable but in general the posterior tip is sharp and the two anterior corners are rounded and meet the blade at about right angles. On mature specimens there is hardly any indication of the development of secondary lateral lobes. As Ziegler (1962a) has indicated, however, there is a complete transition from this basic species to those with well-developed lobes.

OCCURRENCE: Middle *dubia* (=*asymmetrica?*) zone, unnamed Upper Devonian formation, Mary's Mountain, Nevada (Fig. 2); 55 specimens

REPOSITORY: USNM 144308, 144309, 144310, 144311, 144312, 144313, 144314, 144315

Genus *Ancyrognathus* Branson and Mehl, 1934
Type species: *A. symmetricus* Branson and Mehl, 1934
*Ancyrognathus triangularis* Youngquist
(Pl. 2, fig. 5)

*Ancyrognathus triangularis* YOUNGQUIST, 1945, Jour. Paleontology, v. 19, p. 356–357, Pl. 54, fig. 7; FAY, 1952, Univ. Kansas Paleont. Contrib., Vert., art. 3, p. 65; MÜLLER AND MÜLLER, 1957, Jour. Paleontology, v. 31, p. 1097, Pl. 137, figs. 3, 6a, 6b; ZIEGLER, 1958, Hess. Landesamt Boden., Notizbl., Bd. 87, p. 49–51, Pl. 10, figs. 1–8, 12, 15, 20; STOPPEL, 1958, Hess. Landesamt Boden., Notizbl., Bd. 87, p. 96; SCHRIEL, 1958, Deutsch. Geol. Gesell. Zeit., Bd. 110, p. 304; KREBS, 1959, Senckenbergiana Lethaea, Bd. 40, p. 381; ZIEGLER, 1962a, Neues Jahrbuch Geol. Paläont., Abh., Bd. 114, p. 153–154; ETHINGTON AND FURNISH, 1962, Jour. Paleontology, v. 36, p. 1263, Pl. 172, figs. 9, 10; KLAPPER AND FURNISH, 1963, Iowa Acad. Sci., Proc. 1962, v. 69, p. 406, Text-fig. 2, fig. 10; SPASSOV, 1964, Rev. Bulgarian Geol. Soc., v. 25, p. 272, Pl. 2, fig. 5; ETHINGTON, 1965, Jour. Paleontology, v. 39, p. 570–571, Pl. 68, fig. 10; ANDERSON, 1966, Jour. Paleontology, v. 40, p. 404, Pl. 48, figs. 1, 5; GLENISTER AND KLAPPER, 1966, Jour. Paleontology, v. 40, p. 802–803, Pl. 87, figs. 10–13

*Ancyrognathus euglypheus* HASS, 1956, U. S. Geol. Survey Prof. Paper 286, p. 17, Pl. 4, fig. 27; LYS, SERRE, AND DEROO, 1957, Inst. Français Pétrole, Rev., v. 12, p. 796, Pl. 7, fig. 2

*Ancyrognathus* sp. A. HASS, 1956, U. S. Geol. Survey Prof. Paper 286, p. 17, Pl. 4, fig. 1

*Ancyrognathus* cf. *A. iowaensis* LYS, SERRE, AND DEROO, 1957, Inst. Français Pétrole, Rev., v. 12, p. 796, Pl. 7, figs. 3, 4

*Ancyrognathus amana* PANSERI AND BARSOTTI, 1959, Inst. Geol. minero España Notas y comun., no. 55, p. 153–154, Pl. 2, fig. 2

REMARKS: This is the name species of the second of Ziegler's major zones. It is not abundant in the Great Basin Devonian but has been found with other species of the *triangularis* zone in the stratigraphic position marking the zone. It also has been found in the overlying *gigas* zone.

OCCURRENCE: Upper part of the *Ancyrognathus triangularis* zone, sample F-15 in Devils Gate Formation (Fig. 3), upper Guilmette Limestone and lowermost Pilot Shale; lower *gigas* zone in the lower Pilot Shale; figured specimen from sample 12, 0.6 mile southwest of section B, Confusion Range, western Utah (Fig. 7); 5 specimens

REPOSITORY: USNM 144316

Genus *Angulodus* Huddle, 1934
Type species: *A. demissus* Huddle, 1934
*Angulodus demissus* Huddle
(Pl. 2, fig. 12)

*Angulodus demissus* HUDDLE, 1934, Bull. Am. Paleontology, v. 21, no. 72, p. 77, Pl. 10, fig. 15; BISCHOFF AND ZIEGLER, 1957, Hess. Landesamt Boden., Abh., no. 22, p. 43, Pl. 8, fig. 9 (labelled *Angulodus gravis* on explanation of plate); Pl. 20, fig. 1

REMARKS: European students have recorded the occurrence of this species in rocks which range from Middle Devonian (Eifelian) through Upper Devonian. This form has been consistently reported from lower Upper Devonian rocks in this country. The shorter limb has an obvious distal hook with three to four very small denticles; the area underneath the hook is filled by thin lamella which originated from the keel. The species is always strongly arched and not straight as *A. walrathi* (Hibbard).

Some of the material referred to by Hibbard (1927) and by Cooper and Sloss (1943) may belong with this species.

OCCURRENCE: Middle *dubia* (=*asymmetrica?*) zone, unnamed Upper Devonian formation, Mary's Mountain, Nevada (Fig. 2); 12 specimens

REPOSITORY: USNM 144317

Genus *Apatognathus* Branson and Mehl, 1934

Type species: *Apatognathus varians* Branson and Mehl, 1934

*Apatognathus varians* Branson and Mehl

(Pl. 2, fig. 1)

*Apatognathus varians* BRANSON AND MEHL, 1934a, Univ. Missouri Studies, v. 8, p. 201–202, Pl. 17, figs. 1–3; BISCHOFF AND ZIEGLER, 1956, Hess. Landesamt Boden., Notizbl., Bd. 84, p. 145, Pl. 14, fig. 3; KLAPPER, 1958, Jour. Paleontology, v. 32, p. 1085, Pl. 141, figs. 6, 8; ETHINGTON, FURNISH, AND WINGERT, 1961, Jour. Paleontology, v. 35, p. 763, Pl. 90, fig. 11; GLENISTER AND KLAPPER, 1966, Jour. Paleontology, v. 40, p. 803, Pl. 96, figs. 14–16

This well-known species is represented in the Great Basin material by several poorly preserved fragments. A large principal denticle and two limbs which are more or less in the same plane and have the same general construction characterize the species.

OCCURRENCE: *Ancyrognathus triangularis* zone, Guilmette Formation, sample 2, Confusion Range, Utah (Fig. 7); 3 specimens

REPOSITORY: UW 1001

Genus *Bryantodus* Bassler, 1925

Type species: *B. typicus* Bassler, 1925

More than 160 species of this genus have been reported from the Lower Devonian through the Middle Pennsylvanian. A great many of these species are synonyms, as in the past such nondiagnostic items as number of denticles have been used for specific discrimination. Monographic study of species will probably reveal that certain forms are useful index fossils. Four species are described from the Upper Devonian of the Great Basin.

*Bryantodus germanus* Ulrich and Bassler

(Pl. 2, fig. 11)

*Bryantodus germanus* ULRICH AND BASSLER, 1926, U. S. National Museum, Proc., v. 68, art. 12, p. 25, Pl. 10, fig. 18; FAY, 1952, Univ. Kansas Paleont. Contrib., Vert., art. 3, p. 71

(Not) *Bryantodus germanus* HOLMES, 1928, U. S. National Museum Proc., v. 72, art. 5, p. 28, Pl. 10, fig. 5; COOPER, 1931a, Jour. Paleontology, v. 5, p. 146, 151, Pl. 20, fig. 4; HUDDLE, 1934, Bull. Am. Paleontology, v. 21, no. 72, p. 15, 72, Pl. 3, fig. 5; COOPER, 1935, Jour. Paleontology, v. 9, p. 310, Pl. 27, fig. 13; BOND, 1947, Ohio Jour. Sci., v. 47, p. 21, 27, Pl. 2, fig. 8

EMENDED DESCRIPTION: A stout, shallowly arched conodont which is somewhat bowed at mid-length. A strong apical denticle is nearly three times as wide as the adjacent teeth and slightly inclined posteriorly. Denticles of the anterior limb are closely crowded and increase in length and diameter toward the distal end. The teeth of the posterior limb are closely spaced and decrease in size away from the apical denticle so that the last ones in the series are peg-like. A wide ridge on each side continues the entire length of the unit and together they form a flat oral surface which is symmetrically divided by the row of teeth. The aboral surface is dominated by a blunt keel which is continuous except for a central elliptical pit which continues anteriorly and posteriorly for a short distance as a narrow groove on the keel. About half of the aboral surface on either side of the keel is occupied by five concentric striae which represent the attachment area of a basal structure (Gross, 1960).

REMARKS: The Nevada material conforms closely to the type description and illustration although the nodes which were reported on the upper surface by Ulrich and Bassler do not appear here. The illustrated specimen, apparently a gerontic individual, shows crowding of the denticles adjacent to the apical denticle. The basal part of this largest tooth suggests that at least one denticle on each side has been incorporated into it during growth.

*Bryantodus germanus* Holmes, 1928, is a homonym of *B. germanus* Ulrich and Bassler, 1926. The former does not show the pronounced lateral ridges which are the principal character of the specimens to which the name was first assigned.

OCCURRENCE: Middle *dubia* (=*asymmetrica?*) zone, unnamed Upper Devonian formation, Mary's Mountain, Nevada (Fig. 2); 30 specimens

REPOSITORY: USNM 144319

## *?Bryantodus grahami* Stauffer
(Pl. 3, fig. 8)

EMENDED DESCRIPTION: Subequal limbs unite at the crest of a high arch to form an angle of almost 90 degrees. The unit is bowed laterally and the posterior limb is twisted so that its base turns inward toward the distal end. A low knob is present at the tip of the arch on the convex outer face which is not otherwise ornamented. A strong shoulder is developed on the posterior part of the concave inner face and may have a few low nodes along its surface. Anteriorly, this shoulder merges with the lateral surface of the unit. A sharp, aboral keel extends the complete length of the conodont except for a small pit at the point of greatest curvature. Many specimens show a thin translucent material adhering to the middle part of the keel and covering the pit. Anteriorly, the denticles are closely set, circular in cross section, and subequal in length. No apical denticle is present but the three teeth at the highest part of the arch are somewhat larger than all others. Denticles of the posterior limb are somewhat shorter than those of the anterior limb. They are increasingly inclined and become progressively larger toward the posterior tip. Bases of the denticles, which can be seen through the transparent lateral walls, penetrate deeper into the base of the posterior half of the unit than they do anteriorly.

REMARKS: This species is similar to species of *Nothognathella* in the presence of a noded posterior shoulder.

OCCURRENCE: Lower *gigas* zone, Pilot Shale; sample 12, 0.6 mile southwest of section B, Confusion Range, western Utah (Fig. 7); 8 specimens

REPOSITORY: USNM 144320

## *Bryantodus masculus* Youngquist and Miller
(Pl. 3, fig. 10)

*Bryantodus masculus* YOUNGQUIST AND MILLER, 1948, Jour. Paleontology, v. 22, p. 443–444, Pl. 68, fig. 4; FAY, 1952, Univ. Kansas Paleont. Contrib., Vert., art. 3, p. 72

EMENDED DESCRIPTION: Arched, somewhat bowed units whose limbs form an angle of about 135 degrees and are nearly equally long. Sharp-edged, posteriorly inclined, apical denticle is double the width of the other teeth and crowded between those adjacent to it. Denticles of anterior limb are progressively shorter and wider away from the center of the unit. At their point of origin they are nearly normal to the axis of the limb but distally they are curved posteriorly. Teeth of the posterior limb are inclined posteriorly parallel to the apical denticle and are uniform in the series. Both faces of the unit have longitudinal ridges at the base of the teeth. The inner ridge widens to form a narrow platform from the apical denticle to near the end of the posterior limb. This platform may be either smooth or ornamented with a few scattered nodes. No corresponding structure occurs on the outer face although here the ridge may form an aborally directed lip beneath the apical denticle. The sharp aboral keel continues from the anterior extremity to the posterior tip interrupted only by a small subapical pit. A zone of parallel, longitudinal striae on each side of the unit extends from the aboral edge halfway up the lateral ridges at the base of the denticles.

OCCURRENCE: Middle *dubia* (=*asymmetrica?*) zone, unnamed Upper Devonian formation, Mary's Mountain, Nevada (Fig. 2); 25 specimens

REPOSITORY: USNM 144321

*Bryantodus multidens* Ulrich and Bassler
(Pl. 3, fig. 14)

*Bryantodus multidens* ULRICH AND BASSLER, 1926, U. S. National Museum Proc., v. 68, art. 12, p. 22–23, Pl. 6, figs. 15, 16; FAY, 1952, Univ. Kansas Paleont. Contrib., Vert., art. 3, p. 72; BISCHOFF, 1956, Hess. Landesamt Boden., Notizbl., Bd. 84, p. 122–123, Pl. 10, figs. 1, 2; BISCHOFF AND ZIEGLER, 1957, Hess. Landesamt Boden., Abh., no. 22, p. 50; ZIEGLER,1958, Hess. Landesamt Boden., Notizbl., Bd. 87, p. 12, 20, 28, 31, 74; ETHINGTON AND FURNISH, 1962, Jour. Paleontology, v. 36, p. 1265; ETHINGTON, 1965, Jour. Paleontology, v. 39, p. 571
*Bryantodus sp.* PANSERI AND BARSOTTI, 1959, Inst. Geol. minero España Notas y comun., no. 55, p. 155, Pl. 2, fig. 5

REMARKS:    Only a single specimen was found in the collections from the Great Basin. It conforms very closely to the development of the type material illustrated by Ulrich and Bassler.

OCCURRENCE:    This species has been reported to range throughout the lower Upper Devonian *Manticoceras* zone in Europe. North American occurrences are in the uppermost Middle Devonian and the lower Upper Devonian. Upper *Palmatolepis triangularis* zone, Pilot Shale; sample 11 collected 0.6 mile southwest of section C, Confusion Range, western Utah (Fig. 7); 1 specimen

REPOSITORY:    USNM 144322

Genus *Ctenopolygnathus* Müller and Müller, 1957
Type species: *Polygnathus angustdisca* Youngquist, 1945
*Ctenopolygnathus iowaensis* (Youngquist and Peterson)
(Pl. 3, fig. 17)

*Polygnathus iowaensis* YOUNGQUIST AND PETERSON, 1947, Jour. Paleontology, v. 21, p. 250–251, Pl. 36, fig. 17; FAY, 1952, Univ. Kansas Paleont. Contrib., Vert., art. 3, p. 155; ETHINGTON, 1965, Jour. Paleontology, v. 39, p. 582, Pl. 68, fig. 12
*Ctenopolygnathus iowaensis* MÜLLER AND MÜLLER, 1957, Jour. Paleontology, v. 31, p. 1084; CLARK AND BECKER, 1960, Geol. Soc. America Bull., v. 71, p. 1670; ETHINGTON, 1962, New Mexico Geol. Soc., Guidebook, 13th Ann. Field Conf., p. 74

EMENDED DESCRIPTION:    Deep, slightly bowed blade set with slender denticles which are basally crowded but discrete above mid-height. Teeth of the anterior half range in size but are two to four times as large as those posterior to mid-length. One or two teeth at the posterior extremity are laterally compressed, sharp-edged, and longer than their neighbors. Basal position of the blade is somewhat deeper than the denticles immediately above it, throughout its length. Aboral margin and locus of the apices of the denticles thus form complementary sinuous curves in lateral view. Aboral edge takes the form of a sharp keel except for a shallow lozenge-shaped escutcheon located along the zone of greatest curvature of the aboral margin. A narrow concave platform extends posteriorly from mid-length, halfway to the blade's end. Lateral margins of the platform are curved upward and set with a row of nodes or low teeth with apices at about the same elevation as those of the blade. In lateral view, the lower surface of the platform merges with the base of the blade at about half the distance between the level of insertion of the teeth and the aboral margin. The upper part of the unit is smooth, but a band extending the entire length parallel to the aboral margin and beneath the platform is finely striated.

OCCURRENCE:    This species is known in the Sheffield Formation of Iowa and the Martin Limestone of central Arizona. Middle *Palmatolepis triangularis* zone, Devils Gate Formation; sample collected 97 feet above base of sample F-5 of section F, Devils Gate Pass, central Nevada (Fig. 3); 5 specimens

REPOSITORY:    USNM 144323

*Ctenopolygnathus omala* (Cooper)
(Pl. 3, fig. 9)

*Polygnathus omala* COOPER, 1939, Jour. Paleontology, v. 13, p. 401, Pl. 39, figs. 71, 72; FAY, 1952, Univ. Kansas Paleont. Contrib., Vert., art. 3, p. 156
*Polygnathus oxus* COOPER, 1939, Jour. Paleontology, v. 13, p. 402, Pl. 39, figs. 53, 54; FAY, 1952, Univ. Kansas Paleont. Contrib., Vert., art. 3, p. 156
*Ctenopolygnathus omala* MÜLLER AND MÜLLER, 1957, Jour. Paleontology, v. 31, p. 1084
*Ctenopolygnathus oxus* MÜLLER AND MÜLLER, 1957, Jour. Paleontology, v. 31, p. 1084

REMARKS: Material at hand does not have the anterior part of the blade retained, but the size of the platform and its rigid ornamentation agree well with the type of *C. omala*. Cooper's figures (1939) suggest a form with a slightly asymmetrical platform. Our material shows this because the posterior end of one side of the platform is directly opposite the center of the other half.

This species differs from *C. angustdisca* (Youngquist) in relative length of the plate as compared to the blade and in possessing strong rib-like ornamentation. However, it resembles the latter species in the denticulation of the blade. *C. iowaensis* (Youngquist and Peterson) has a much deeper blade, and ornamentation of the platform is restricted to nodes or small denticles along the upturned margins.

OCCURRENCE: Middle *dubia* (=*asymmetrica?*) zone, unnamed Upper Devonian formation, Mary's Mountain, Nevada (Fig. 2); 4 specimens

REPOSITORY: USNM 144324

Genus *Diplododella* Bassler, 1925
Type species: *D. bilateralis* Bassler, 1925
*Diplododella alternata* Branson and Mehl
(Pl. 3, fig. 7)

*Diplodella alternata* (sic) BRANSON AND MEHL, 1934a, Univ. Missouri Studies, v. 8, p. 204, Pl. 16, figs. 23, 24
*Diplododella alternata* FAY, 1952, Univ. Kansas Paleont. Contrib., Vert., art. 3, p. 86
REMARKS: The Nevada material agrees closely with the type material from the Saverton Formation of Missouri in the conformation and denticulation of the limbs. The posterior bar is deeper and narrower than that on the type specimen. In transmitted light many slender unerupted denticles which extend almost to the base can be seen within the bar.

OCCURRENCE: Middle *dubia* (=*asymmetrica?*) zone, unnamed Upper Devonian formation, Mary's Mountain, Nevada (Fig. 2); 14 specimens

REPOSITORY: USNM 144325

Genus *Enantiognathus* Mosher and Clark, 1965
Type species: *Apatognathus inversa* Sannemann, 1955

This genus was proposed to include species which are distinguished from the highly arched yet straight limbs of forms assigned to *Apatognathus* by a strong posterior direction of the two limbs. The two strongly inwardly flexed limbs along with a high principal denticle serve to differentiate *Enantiognathus* from *Gnamptognathus*, as well.

Species are known to range from the Upper Devonian into the Permian (Clark and Ethington, 1963) and Triassic (*e. g.*, Mosher and Clark, 1965).

*Enantiognathus lipperti* (Bischoff)
(Pl. 2, fig. 2)

*Apatognathus lipperti* BISCHOFF, 1956, Hess. Landesamt Boden., Notizbl., Bd. 84, p. 116, 121–122, Pl. 9, figs. 27, 31; BISCHOFF AND ZIEGLER, 1956, Hess. Landesamt Boden., Notizbl., Bd. 84, p. 143, 145, Pl. 14, figs. 1, 2; BISCHOFF AND ZIEGLER, 1957, Hess. Landesamt Boden., Abh., no. 22, p. 38, 39, 45; LYS AND SERRE, 1957a, Inst. Français Pétrole, Rev., v. 12, p. 1040, Pl. 1, fig. 4; ZIEGLER, 1958, Hess. Landesamt Boden., Notizbl., Bd. 87, p. 12, 20, 28, 31, 56, Pl. 12, figs. 10, 22; STOPPEL, 1958, Hess. Landesamt Boden., Notizbl., Bd. 87, p. 94; HELMS, 1959, Geologie, v. 8, Pl. 1, fig. 16; SCOTT AND COLLINSON, 1961, Kansas Geol. Soc., Guidebook, 26th Annual Field Conf., p. 113, 115, 122, Pl. 10, fig. 2; ETHINGTON AND FURNISH, 1962, Jour. Paleontology, v. 36, p. 1264, Pl. 173, fig. 16
*Apatognathus* cf. *A. lipperti* LYS, SERRE, AND DEROO, 1957, Inst. Français Pétrole, Rev., v. 12, p. 797, Pl. 7, fig. 7
*Gnamptognathus ? lipperti* GLENISTER AND KLAPPER, 1966, Jour. Paleontology, v. 40, p. 803–804, Pl. 96, figs. 10–12
*? Gnamptognathus ?* cf. *G. ? lipperti* GLENISTER AND KLAPPER, 1966, Jour. Paleontology, v. 40, p. 804, Pl. 96, fig. 13

REMARKS: No complete specimens were recovered and in all specimens the distal part of both limbs is broken. However, the denticulation of the limbs and their relationship to the apical denticle are so distinctive that the species can be readily recognized even from fragments.

OCCURRENCE: In Europe the species is common in the lowermost Upper Devonian. The only previously reported occurrence in North America is in the Louisiana Limestone of Illinois and Missouri. Lower *gigas* zone, Pilot Shale; sample 12, 0.6 mile southwest of section B, Confusion Range, western Utah (Fig. 7); 4 specimens

REPOSITORY: USNM 144318

Genus *Hindeodella* Bassler, 1925
Type species: *H. subtilis* Bassler, 1925

The numerous species of this genus have been reported from Silurian through Triassic rocks. Because the long delicate blades of the species are commonly broken, specific identification is usually difficult and "lumping" as well as "splitting" seems to be the rule in taxonomy for this group. Some of the more obvious synonyms are indicated herein.

*Hindeodella minuta* Branson and Mehl
(Pl. 3, fig. 18)

*Hindeodella minuta* BRANSON AND MEHL, 1934a, Univ. Missouri Studies, v. 8, p. 196, Pl. 14, fig. 9; FAY, 1952, Univ. Kansas Paleont. Contrib., Vert., art. 3, p. 105

EMENDED DESCRIPTION: Posterior bar arched and slightly twisted toward distal end. Cusp somewhat posterior to juncture of lateral process with posterior bar; subcircular in cross section and posteriorly inclined. Five to six discrete denticles of posterior bar are nearly uniform in size and inclined parallel to the cusp. Lateral process curves through a right angle with axis of the posterior bar. Teeth on the process decrease in size toward the distal extremity. Aboral edges sharp with a narrow, short groove at the juncture of posterior bar and lateral process. A zone of parallel striae extends up each side of bar and process nearly to the base of the denticles.

REMARKS: A gerontic specimen in the collection has denticles which become sharp-edged and closely crowded late in the ontogeny. On most of the material the teeth are separated by a small space or are just in contact at their base. Although germ denticles could be seen within the bar alternating in position with the principal teeth, none were erupted.

OCCURRENCE: Middle *Palmatolepis triangularis* zone, Pilot Shale; sample 21, 3½ miles southwest of section C, Confusion Range, western Utah (Fig. 7); 8 specimens

REPOSITORY: USNM 144326

*Hindeodella subtilis* Bassler
(Pl. 3, fig. 15)

*Hindeodella subtilis* BASSLER, 1925, Geol. Soc. America Bull., v. 36, p. 219; FAY, 1952, Univ. Kansas Paleont. Contrib., Vert., art. 3, p. 106; BISCHOFF, 1956, Hess. Landesamt Boden., Notizbl., Bd. 84, p. 117, 124; BISCHOFF AND ZIEGLER, 1956, Hess. Landesamt. Boden., Notizbl., p. 147; ZIEGLER, 1958, Hess. Landesamt Boden., Notizbl., Bd. 87, p. 12, 20, 28, 31, 74; STOPPEL, 1958, Hess. Landesamt Boden., Notizbl., Bd. 87, p. 94; ETHINGTON AND FURNISH, 1962, Jour. Paleontology, v. 36, p. 1267; ETHINGTON, 1965, Jour. Paleontology, v. 39, p. 572

*Hindeodella crassidens* COOPER, 1931b, Jour. Paleontology, v. 5, p. 236, Pl. 28, fig. 16; FAY, 1952, Univ. Kansas Paleont. Contrib., Vert., art. 3, p. 103

*Hindeodella petila* COOPER, 1931b, Jour. Paleontology, v. 5, p. 237–238, Pl. 28, fig. 21; FAY, 1952, Univ. Kansas Paleont. Contrib., Vert., art. 3, p. 105–106

*Hindeodella delicatula* STAUFFER AND PLUMMER, 1932, Univ. Texas Bull., no. 3201, p. 34, Pl. 1, figs. 3, 7; FAY, 1952, Univ. Kansas Paleont. Contrib., Vert., art. 3, p. 104 (not BRANSON AND MEHL, 1934b, Univ. Missouri Studies, v. 8, p. 280, Pl. 22, fig. 30)

*Hindeodella diseriata* STAUFFER AND PLUMMER, 1932, Univ. Texas Bull., no. 3201, p. 34, Pl. 1, figs. 8, 10, 16, 17; FAY, 1952, Univ. Kansas Paleont. Contrib., Vert., art. 3, p. 104

*Hindeodella irregularis* STAUFFER AND PLUMMER, 1932, Univ. Texas Bull., no. 3201, Pl. 1, figs. 8, 10, 16, 17; FAY, 1952, Univ. Kansas Paleont. Contrib., Vert., art. 3, p. 104

*Hindeodella* sp. A, B, C, D, F STAUFFER AND PLUMMER, 1932, Univ. Texas Bull., no. 3201, p. 35–36, Pl. 1, figs. 11, 13, 14, 15, 18

*Hindeodella aculeata* HUDDLE, 1934, Bull. Am. Paleontology, v. 21, no. 72, p. 14, 27, 40–41, 43, Pl. 4, figs. 19–21, Pl. 5, figs. 2, 3; FAY, 1952, Univ. Kansas Paleont. Contrib., Vert., art. 3, p. 102

*Hindeodella alternidens* HUDDLE, 1934, Bull. Am. Paleontology, v. 21, no. 72, p. 14, 44, 47, Pl. 5, figs. 12–13; FAY, 1952, Univ. Kansas Paleont. Contrib., Vert., art. 3, p. 102

*Hindeodella angulus* HUDDLE, 1934, Bull. Am. Paleontology, v. 21, no. 72, p. 14, 44, Pl. 5, fig. 14

*Hindeodella elongata* HUDDLE, 1934, Bull. Am. Paleontology, v. 21, no. 72, p. 14, 42, Pl. 5, figs. 5–6; FAY, 1952, Univ. Kansas Paleont. Contrib., Vert., art. 3, p. 104

*Hindeodella gracilis* HUDDLE, 1934, Bull. Am. Paleontology, v. 21, no. 72, p. 14, 43, Pl. 5, fig. 11; FAY, 1952, Univ. Kansas Paleont. Contrib., Vert., art. 3, p. 104

*Hindeodella delicatula* BRANSON AND MEHL, 1934b, Univ. Missouri Studies, v. 8, p. 280, Pl. 22, fig. 30; FAY, 1952, Univ. Kansas Paleont. Contrib., Vert., art. 3, p. 104

*Hindeodella gladiola* E. R. BRANSON, 1934, Univ. Missouri Studies, v. 8, p. 324, Pl. 28, fig. 18; FAY, 1952, Univ. Kansas Paleont. Contrib., Vert., art. 3, p. 104

*Hindeodella beta* STAUFFER, 1938, Jour. Paleontology, v. 12, p. 412, 427, Pl. 50, figs. 16, 19

*Hindeodella conferta* STAUFFER, 1938, Jour. Paleontology, v. 12, p. 412, 427, Pl. 50, figs. 21–22; FAY, 1952, Univ. Kansas Paleont. Contrib., Vert., art. 3, p. 103

*Hindeodella lambtonensis* STAUFFER, 1938, Jour. Paleontology, v. 12, p. 412, 428, Pl. 50, figs. 2, 5, 8, 13–14, 17, 20, 25, 28, 31; FAY, 1952, Univ. Kansas Paleont. Contrib., Vert., art. 3, p. 105

*Hindeodella milleri* STAUFFER, 1938, Jour. Paleontology, v. 12, p. 412, 428, Pl. 50, figs. 1, 3a, 3b, 4, 9–11; FAY, 1952, Univ. Kansas Paleont. Contrib., Vert., art. 3, p. 105

*Hindeodella modesta* STAUFFER, 1938, Jour. Paleontology, v. 12, p. 412, 428, Pl. 50, figs. 7, 23, 24a, 24b, 27, 30

*Hindeodella priscilla* STAUFFER, 1938, Jour. Paleontology, v. 12, p. 412, 429, Pl. 50, fig. 6; FAY, 1952, Univ. Kansas Paleont. Contrib., Vert., art. 3, p. 106; LYS AND SERRE, 1957a, Inst. Français Pétrole, Rev., v. 12, p. 1044, Pl. 3, fig. 2

*Hindeodella austinensis* STAUFFER, 1940, Jour. Paleontology, v. 14, p. 424, Pl. 58, figs. 3–7, 9; FAY, 1952, Univ. Kansas Paleont. Contrib., Vert., art. 3, p. 103; SERRE AND LYS, 1960, 21st Internat. Geol. Cong., Rept., pt. 6, p. 38

*Hindeodella moweri* STAUFFER, 1940, Jour. Paleontology, v. 14, p. 424, Pl. 58, figs. 2, 10–11; FAY, 1952, Univ. Kansas Paleont. Contrib., Vert., art. 3, p. 105

*Hindeodella germana* LYS, SERRE, AND DEROO, 1957, Inst. Français Pétrole, Rev., v. 12, p. 800, Pl. 8, fig. 7; LYS AND SERRE, 1957a, Inst. Français Pétrole, Rev., v. 12, p. 1044, Pl. 3, fig. 2

*Hindeodella* sp. RHODES AND DINELEY, 1957, Jour. Paleontology, v. 31, p. 362, Pl. 37, figs. 6–10 (not Pl. 38, fig. 2)

REMARKS: This species is characterized by alternation in size of denticles along a slender bar. The original description cited three smaller teeth alternating with each larger pair although deviations from this number were mentioned. Numerous species have been proposed, many based on very fragmented material which differed only in having fewer or more of the small denticles in each space. The Great Basin collection shows that this is a character that varies with position along the bar and from one growth stage to another. Thus, many of the species which have been described are probably junior synonyms of *H. subtilis*. Detailed descriptions are needed for all Devonian–Pennsylvanian occurrences in view of multi-element species concept.

OCCURRENCE: This species has been found in the *A. triangularis* zone through the *crepida* zone in the Devils Gate Limestone from Nevada and the Pilot Shale in western Utah and is present in most of the conodont-bearing samples of this interval. Some of the better material is from sample C-19, top of F-16, F-5, 11, 21 (*see* Table 1 for locality data); 68 specimens

REPOSITORY: USNM 144327

### *Hindeodella unca* Bischoff
(Pl. 4, fig. 1)

*Hindeodella unca* BISCHOFF, 1956, Hess. Landesamt Boden., Notizbl., Bd. 84, p. 124–125, Pl. 10, fig. 37–41

REMARKS: Specimens in the Mary's Mountain collection fit the description of Bischoff for this species with little or no variation. The elongate posterior-projecting denticle is preserved on only a few specimens and when it is broken it becomes difficult to distinguish this species from others of the genus.

OCCURRENCE: Middle *dubia* (=*asymmetrica?*) zone, unnamed Upper Devonian formation, Mary's Mountain, Nevada (Fig. 2); 5 specimens

REPOSITORY: USNM 144341

## Genus *Icriodus* Branson and Mehl, 1938
Type species: *I. expansus* Branson and Mehl, 1938

Müller (1962, p. 113, 114) has indicated that *Icriodus* developed from *Spathognathodus* late in the Silurian. He removed Lower and Middle Devonian forms such as *Icriodus latericrescens*, which is characterized by the presence of lateral limbs or branches, to a new genus, *Latericriodus*.

Icriodids which were not specifically identified have been recorded from rocks as young as middle Late Devonian in Europe (Schriel and Stoppel, 1960), but the youngest species described there occurs in early Late Devonian strata characterized by the ammonoid *Cheiloceras* (Stoppel, 1958). Collinson and others (1962) indicated that the upper limit of the range of *Icriodus* in North America coincides with that of the ammonoid *Manticoceras* and that the few specimens found in younger strata were reworked.

A single specimen from the Lower Triassic of the Butte Mountains of Nevada appears similar to *Icriodus* (Clark and others, 1964) but no other specimens have been reported from rocks younger than Devonian.

Six species are described.

### *Icriodus cornutus* Sannemann
(Pl. 3, figs. 3, 4)

*Icriodus cornutus* SANNEMANN, 1955a, Senckenbergiana Lethaea, Bd. 36, p. 130, Pl. 4, figs. 19a–c, 20, 21; BISCHOFF, 1956, Hess. Landesamt Boden., Notizbl., Bd. 84, p. 117, 125, Pl. 10, fig. 42; BISCHOFF AND ZIEGLER, 1956, Hess. Landesamt Boden., Notizbl., Bd. 84, p. 143, 147; FLÜGEL AND ZIEGLER, 1957, Naturw. Ver. Steiermark, Mitt., Bd. 87, Table 1; ZIEGLER, 1958, Hess. Landesamt Boden., Notizbl., Bd. 87, p. 20, 31, 74; STOPPEL, 1958, Hess. Landesamt Boden., Notizbl., Bd. 87, p. 101; ZIEGLER, 1959, Neues Jahrbuch Geol. Paläont., Monatsh., Bd. 7, p. 300; HELMS, 1959, Geologie, v. 8, no. 6, p. 642; ASH, 1961, Micropaleontology, v. 7, p. 232; ETHINGTON AND FURNISH, 1962, Jour. Paleontology, v. 36, p. 1269, Pl. 172, figs. 7, 8; ETHINGTON, 1965, Jour. Paleontology, v. 39, p. 574; GLENISTER AND KLAPPER, 1966, Jour. Paleontology, v. 40, p. 804–805, Pl. 95, figs. 2, 3
*Icriodus* cf. *I. alternatus* LYS AND SERRE, 1957a, Inst. Français Pétrole, Rev., v. 12, p. 1044, Pl. 3, figs. 5a, 5b; ZIEGLER, 1962b, Hess. Landesamt Boden., Abh., no. 38, p. 52
*Icriodus* sp. HASS, 1959, U. S. Geol. Survey Prof. Paper 294-J, Pl. 50, fig. 2

EMENDED DESCRIPTION: Slender, slightly curved icriodids in which the denticles of the central row alternate in position with those of the two outer series. Teeth of the lateral rows are, for the most part, stout cones, although some are chisel-shaped and slightly rotated so that their sharp oral edges are arranged at an angle to the axis of the unit. The denticles in the center row are laterally compressed and smaller than the adjacent outer teeth. A proclined cusp is located anteriorly in line with the middle series of teeth. In lateral view, the aboral margin is parallel to the oral surface except at the anterior end beneath the cusp where it turns downward.

Aborally, the unit is excavated by a V-shaped trough which is widely expanded beneath the anterior cusp but is regularly tapered toward the posterior end.

REMARKS: Alternating position of denticles between the middle and outer rows is suggestive of *Icriodus alternatus*. However, the latter species does not possess a cusp and its base is not broadly expanded anteriorly. Glenister and Klapper (1966, p. 805) have suggested that the strongly inclined main cusp may be a critical feature in distinguishing *I. cornutus* from *I. alternatus*. These same writers have indicated that they believe the two species are transitional (p. 805). Of the specimens available for this study, none that have a strong cusp lack a broadly expanded cavity anteriorly. Because this feature apparently is not present on *I. alternatus*, we have used its presence as a determining factor in the identification of *I. cornutus*. If these two species are indeed transitional, none of these characteristics may serve as objective criteria for differentiation. If this proves to be the case, the two should be considered synonyms.

Anderson (1966, p. 407) has suggested that *I. cornutus* is a junior synonym of *I. rectus* Youngquist and Peterson. This writer has pointed out that the range in variation of *I. rectus* in abundant Iowa material would encompass characteristics of *I. cornutus*. Obviously, there is no widespread agreement on the *I. cornutus-alternatus-rectus* group (Glenister and Klapper, 1966, p. 804–805; Anderson, 1966, p. 407; this report) and a monographic study is necessary to resolve the problems.

OCCURRENCE: Specimens from the Devils Gate Limestone compare very closely to Sannemann's figured types. Although not previously recorded from North America, this species has been widely reported in the Upper Devonian of Europe where it occurs in highest Frasnian and in Famennian strata. Middle *Palmatolepis triangularis* zone; Devils Gate Limestone, sample F-6 of section F, Devils Gate Pass, Nevada (Fig. 3) and Pilot Shale, sample 21, 3½ miles southwest of section C, Confusion Range, western Utah (Fig. 7); 9 specimens

REPOSITORY: USNM 144328, 144329

### *Icriodus curvatus* Branson and Mehl
### (Pl. 3, fig. 13)

*Icriodus curvatus* BRANSON AND MEHL, 1938, Jour. Paleontology, v. 12, p. 162–163, Pl. 26, figs. 23–26; FAY, 1952, Univ. Kansas Paleont. Contrib., Vert., art. 3, p. 109; GRAVES, 1952, Jour. Paleontology, v. 26, p. 612, Pl. 81, figs. 10, 11; ZIEGLER, 1956, Hess. Landesamt Boden., Notizbl., Bd. 84, p. 94, 95, 96, 97, 98, 100, Pl. 6. figs. 22–24; BISCHOFF AND ZIEGLER, 1956, Hess. Landesamt Boden., Notizbl., Bd. 84, p. 147, Table 1; FLÜGEL AND ZIEGLER, 1957, Naturw. Ver. Steiermark, Mitt., Bd. 87, Table 1; LYS AND SERRE, 1957a, Inst. Français Pétrole, Rev., v. 12, p. 1037, 1044–1045, Pl. 3, figs. 6a, 6b; LYS AND SERRE, 1957b, Acad. Sci. Comptes Rendus, v. 244, p. 917; BISCHOFF AND ZIEGLER, 1957, Hess. Landesamt Boden., Abh., no. 22, p. 19, 32, 33, 37, 39, 61–62, 125, 126, 130, Pl. 6, figs. 6a, 6b; SCHRIEL AND STOPPEL, 1958a, Deutsch. Geol. Gesell. Zeit., Bd. 109, p. 299, 302; SCHRIEL AND STOPPEL, 1958b, Deutsch. Geol. Gesell. Zeit., Bd. 110, p. 273, 275; BISCHOFF AND SANNEMANN, 1958, Hess. Landesamt Boden., Notizbl., Bd. 86, p. 91, 95; ZIEGLER, 1958, Hess. Landesamt Boden., Notizbl., Bd. 87, p. 12, 20, 28, 31, 74; STOPPEL, 1958, Hess. Landesamt Boden., Notizbl., Bd. 87, p. 95, 96, 101, 105; SCHRIEL AND STOPPEL, 1960, Deutsch. Geol. Gesell. Zeit., Bd. 111, p. 668; CLARK AND BECKER, 1960, Geol. Soc. America Bull., v. 71, p. 1670; SERRE AND LYS, 1960, 21st Internat. Geol. Cong., Rept., pt. 6, p. 38; CLARK AND ETHINGTON, 1966, Jour. Paleontology, v. 40, p. 680, Pl. 83, fig. 8

OCCURRENCE: European workers have recorded *Icriodus curvatus* in rocks ranging from late Early Devonian to early Late Devonian. Only a single report of this species in Early Devonian rocks of this country is available. However, there have been very few conodont studies on the Lower and Middle Devonian of North America. *Rhomboidea* zone, Devils Gate Limestone; sample E-1 of section E, Diamond Mountains, Nevada (Fig. 4); 1 specimen

REPOSITORY: USNM 144330

### *Icriodus elegantulus* Stauffer

*Icriodus elegantulus* STAUFFER, 1938, Jour. Paleontology, v. 12, p. 430, Pl. 52, figs. 26, 27; FAY, 1952, Univ. Kansas Paleont. Contrib., Vert., art. 3, p. 110

REMARKS: This species is distinct from other icriodids in the marked contrast in size between the denticles of the medial row and those of the two lateral series. On the specimens present in the Great Basin material, the oral surface is a broad longitudinal trough between outer rows of heavy teeth. The denticles of the center row are reduced to a series of low, conical nodes alternating in position with those on either side. Lateral teeth are for the most part discrete and tend to be somewhat compressed in the anteroposterior direction, giving some of them a chisel edge. The inner side of most teeth is slightly rotated posteriorly so that they stand at an angle to the axis of the unit. Sides of the conodont are nearly vertical and the entire unit is slightly curved along its length. Most of the cusp on studied specimens has been lost, but the stub which remains suggests that it was heavy and strongly inclined in the anterior direction. The basal groove is narrow with steep walls except beneath the anterior part of the unit.

OCCURRENCE: Lower *Palmatolepis triangularis* zone, Pilot Shale; sample from lower part of B-34 of section B, Confusion Range, western Utah (Fig. 5); 5 specimens

REPOSITORY: USNM 144331

### *Icriodus expansus* Branson and Mehl
### (Pl. 3, figs. 1, 2)

*Icriodus expansus* BRANSON AND MEHL, 1938, Jour. Paleontology, v. 12, p. 160, Pl. 26, figs. 18–21; ELLISON AND WYNN, 1950, Am. Jour. Sci., v. 248, p. 795, Pl. 1, figs. 29, 30, 32, 34, 35; FAY, 1952, Univ. Kansas Paleont. Contrib., Vert., art. 3, p. 110; LYS AND SERRE, 1957a, Inst. Français Pétrole, Rev., v. 12, p. 1045–1046, Pl. 4, figs. 1a, 1b; MÜLLER AND MÜLLER, 1957, Jour. Paleontology, v. 31, p. 1106, Pl. 142, fig. 4; ZIEGLER, 1958, Hess. Landesamt Boden., Notizbl., Bd. 87, p. 12, 20, 28, 31, 74; ZIEGLER, 1959, Neues Jahrbuch Paläont., Monatsh., Bd. 7, p. 300; SERRE AND LYS, 1960, 21st Internat. Geol. Cong., Rept., pt. 6, p. 38

*Icriodus subterminus* YOUNGQUIST, 1947, Jour. Paleontology, v. 21, p. 103, Pl. 25, fig. 14

*Icriodus* sp. HASS, 1956, U. S. Geol. Survey Prof. Paper 286, Pl. 4, fig. 6

*Icriodus nodosus* ZIEGLER, 1956, Hess. Landesamt Boden., Notizbl., Bd. 84, p. 102, Pl. 6, figs. 18–21; BISCHOFF AND ZIEGLER, 1957, Hess. Landesamt Boden., Abh., no. 22, p. 62, Pl. 6, figs. 2, 35, Pl. 19, figs. 1–5; BUDUROV, 1961, Rev. Bulgarian Geol. Soc., v. 22, p. 263, Pl. 2, figs. 1-3a, b; 5a-c; 8a-b; 11a-c; 12a-b; 13a-c

REMARKS: Branson and Mehl (1938, p. 160) redefined *Gondolella? nodosa* Huddle as an icriodid and stated that it can be differentiated from *I. expansus* primarily in having a slender rather than biconvex outline. They also observed that the aboral margin is abruptly offset near the anterior end in *I. nodosus*, whereas in the type species, the base widens uniformly away from the posterior extremity. They further described *I. expansus* as a very variable species, largely in its tendency to develop transverse barlike denticles in the lateral series, which may be fused to the corresponding teeth of the middle row.

Icriodids from the Mary's Mountain exposures include forms encompassing the range of variation outlined for *I. expansus*. Oral outline of most individuals is relatively slender but on some is distinctly biconvex. Most show a flexure of one lateral wall about one third their length from the anterior end, thus producing an offset in the basal outline. In some cases, this is extreme and the deflected margin is nearly normal to the axis of the unit. However, a complete series of gradational forms exists between such specimens and others which exhibit no sudden basal expansion. Most specimens are straight, but a few are distinctly bowed near the posterior end. About one third of the material has the denticles of the lateral rows joined to those of the middle series to form transverse ridges.

Although the extreme specimens in the collection can be identified with *I. nodosus* or *I. expansus*, respectively, the majority of them fall between the two species in the development of their characters and no distinct separation is possible. All are here placed in *I. expansus* because of the fragmentary and uncertain nature of the type material of *I. nodosus*. The possibility exists that the holotype of the latter species falls within the apparently considerable range of variation of *I. expansus* and that the two are conspecific.

OCCURRENCE: Middle *dubia* (= *asymmetrica?*) zone, unnamed Upper Devonian formation, Mary's Mountain, Nevada (Fig. 2); 40 specimens

REPOSITORY: USNM 144332, 144333

### *Icriodus parvus* Youngquist and Peterson
### (Pl. 3, fig. 11)

*Icriodus parvus* YOUNGQUIST AND PETERSON, 1947, Jour. Paleontology, v. 21, p. 248, Pl. 37, figs. 11, 12; FAY, 1952, Univ. Kansas Paleont. Contrib., Vert., art. 3, p. 110

EMENDED DESCRIPTION: Icriodids characterized by very irregular denticulation and a broadly flared base beneath the anterior half of the unit. Anteriorly, above the expanded base, the denticles are developed as sharp-edged transverse ribs which may be discrete or connected at their mid-points by a longitudinal ridge. Three such ridges are present on specimens studied. On the posterior half of the unit, the denticles take the form of chisel-like elevations whose inner sides approximate the mid-line of the conodont. These teeth are almost all found on one flank of the unit with only one or two located on the opposite side so that, in oral view, the conodont is decidedly asymmetrical posterior to mid-length. Some of the denticles show a low sag in the center of their oral edge, suggesting that they represent two nearly completely fused teeth which were arranged side by side. The anterior margin of the unit is nearly vertical and forms almost a right angle with the sharp oral edge. The basal cavity is a broad trough which is widely expanded anteriorly.

REMARKS: The material from Utah agrees with most characteristics of the type description but Youngquist and Peterson reported that no expanded base was present on the type specimen. Study of the Utah material indicates that the thin-walled basal part of most icriodids is quite fragile and more or less broken on many specimens. The figured type of this species appears to be somewhat fragmented and it is likely that the basal region of the specimen was lost.

OCCURRENCE: Middle *Palmatolepis triangularis* zone, Pilot Shale; sample 21 from $3\frac{1}{2}$ miles southwest of section C, Confusion Range, western Utah (Fig. 7); 3 specimens

REPOSITORY: USNM 144334

*Icriodus rectus* Youngquist and Peterson

(Pl. 3, fig. 16)

*Icriodus rectus* YOUNGQUIST AND PETERSON, 1947, Jour. Paleontology, v. 21, p. 248, Pl. 37, figs. 3, 4, 13, 14, 26; FAY, 1952, Univ. Kansas Paleont. Contrib., Vert., art. 3, p. 110; ANDERSON, 1966, Jour. Paleontology, v. 40, p. 406–407

EMENDED DESCRIPTION: Deep, slender icriodids that tend to be slightly bowed along their length. Denticles of the oral edge are arranged in three parallel series above the central part of the unit. Teeth of the center row are joined to each other by a sharp ridge. Those of the lateral series are connected to the denticles of the middle row so that the resultant triad forms distinct ridges transverse to the axis of the unit. Four such ridges are present on all specimens at hand. The center series of denticles is not present at the posterior end of the unit. In this region, the lateral teeth are wedge-shaped and somewhat offset on opposite sides of the conodont. Some are slightly rotated so that they form acute angles with the long axis of the specimen. The central row of teeth continues anteriorly beyond the lateral series for the space of two denticles. These are low, circular in section, and inclined anteriorly. The aboral surface is deeply excavated along the entire length, with greatest depth attained somewhat posterior to the base of the front denticle.

REMARKS: Both juvenile and mature specimens are present in the material at hand. The fusion of denticles into ridges is clearly shown even on the most immature individuals. Growth tends to make these teeth increasingly obscure so that the longitudinal arrangement of denticles, which is characteristic of the genus, is largely masked by the development of the transverse ribs. Interconnections of the denticles are found on *Icriodus curvatus*; Branson and Mehl (1938) reported a tendency toward the formation of transverse ridges. However, in this species the teeth always maintain their individuality within their respective series.

Comments concerning this species, in view of remarks of Anderson (1966, p. 407), are found under discussion of *I. cornutus*.

OCCURRENCE: Upper *Palmatolepis triangularis* zone, Pilot Shale; sample 11 from 0.6 mile southwest of section C, Confusion Range, western Utah (Fig. 7); 14 specimens

REPOSITORY: USNM 144335

Genus *Ligonodina* Bassler, 1925

Type species: *L. pectinata* Bassler, 1925

*Ligonodina acuta* Branson and Mehl

(Pl. 3, fig. 5)

*Ligonodina acuta* BRANSON AND MEHL, 1934a, Univ. Missouri Studies, v. 8, p. 200, Pl. 15, fig. 32; FAY, 1952, Univ. Kansas Paleont. Contrib., Vert., art. 3, p. 116

REMARKS: A single representative of this species conforms closely to the type material from the Saverton Formation of Missouri in the development of the aboral edge. The illustrated type does not show more than a stump of the denticles of the posterior bar but they appear to be nearly erect. On the Utah specimen the teeth of the bar are inclined posteriorly at an angle of about 45 degrees.

OCCURRENCE: Upper *Palmatolepis triangularis* zone, Pilot Shale; sample 11 from 0.6 mile southwest of section C, Confusion Range, western Utah (Fig. 7); one specimen

REPOSITORY: USNM 144336

### *Ligonodina delicata* Branson and Mehl
(Pl. 3, fig. 6)

*Ligonodina delicata* BRANSON AND MEHL, 1934a, Univ. Missouri Studies, v. 8, p. 199, Pl. 14, figs. 22, 23; FAY, 1952, Univ. Kansas Paleont. Contrib., Vert., art. 3, p. 117; BISCHOFF, 1956, Hess. Landesamt Boden., Notizbl., Bd. 84, p. 117, 126, Pl. 10, fig. 14; BISCHOFF AND ZIEGLER, 1956, Hess. Landesamt Boden., Notizbl., Bd. 84, p. 148; FLÜGEL AND ZIEGLER, 1957, Naturw. Ver. Steiermark, Mitt., Bd. 87, p. 43, Pl. 5, fig. 13; BISCHOFF AND ZIEGLER, 1957, Hess. Landesamt Boden., Abh., no. 22, p. 31, 32, 33, 37, 39, 64; ZIEGLER, 1958, Hess. Landesamt Boden., Notizbl., Bd. 87, p. 12, 20, 28, 31, 74; KREBS, 1959, Senckenbergiana Lethaea, Bd. 40, p. 373; SERRE AND LYS, 1960, 21st Internat. Geol. Cong., Rept., pt. 6, p. 38; ETHINGTON AND FURNISH, 1962, Jour. Paleontology, v. 36, p. 1271; SPASSOV, 1964, Rev. Bulgarian Geol. Soc., v. 25, p. 274, Pl. 2, fig. 13; SPASSOV, 1965, Trav. Géol. Bulgarie, sér. Paléont., v. 7, p. 87–88, Pl. 1, figs. 12, 13; ETHINGTON, 1965, Jour. Paleontology, v. 39, p. 575

*Ligonodina delicatula* COOPER, 1939, Jour. Paleontology, v. 13, p. 390, 419, Pl. 45, figs. 50, 60, 61

*Ligonodina recurvata* MILLER AND YOUNGQUIST, 1947, Jour. Paleontology, v. 21, p. 510, Pl. 73, fig. 20

*Ligonodina hindei ?* LYS, SERRE, AND DEROO, 1957, Inst. Français Pétrole., Rev., v. 12, p. 801–802, Pl. 10, fig. 1

REMARKS: This species is very similar to *L. acuta* in the denticulation of the posterior bar and the position and configuration of the anterior aboral process. However, *L. delicata* is grooved aborally beneath both bar and process with greatest width and depth of the excavation attained beneath the cusp.

OCCURRENCE: Middle *dubia* (= *asymmetrica?*) zone, unnamed Upper Devonian formation, Mary's Mountain, Nevada (Fig. 2); lower *gigas* zone, sample 12 which is 0.6 mile southwest of section B, and upper *Palmatolepis triangularis* zone, sample 11 which is 0.6 mile southwest of section C, Confusion Range, western Utah (Fig. 7); 4 specimens

REPOSITORY: USNM 144337

### Genus *Lonchodina* Bassler, 1925
Type species: *L. typicalis* Bassler, 1925

Species have been reported from the Silurian through the Triassic. There is considerable variation in reported species and detailed investigation may reveal specific refinement. Six species are recognized in the Great Basin Upper Devonian.

### *Lonchodina acutula* Huddle
(Pl. 3, fig. 12)

*Lonchodina acutula* HUDDLE, 1934, Bull. Am. Paleontology, v. 21, no. 72, p. 85, Pl. 6, fig. 14; FAY, 1952, Univ. Kansas Paleont. Contrib., Vert., art. 3, p. 121; ETHINGTON AND FURNISH, 1962, Jour. Paleontology, v. 36, p. 1272

REMARKS: A single individual from Nevada seems identical with specimens previously assigned to this species.

OCCURRENCE: Middle *dubia* (= *asymmetrica?*) zone, unnamed Upper Devonian formation, Mary's Mountain, Nevada (Fig. 2); 1 specimen

REPOSITORY: USNM 144338

*Lonchodina arcuata* Ulrich and Bassler

(Pl. 5, fig. 6)

*Lonchodina arcuata* ULRICH AND BASSLER, 1926, U. S. National Museum, Proc., v. 68, art. 12, p. 32, Pl. 5, fig. 15; FAY, 1952, Univ. Kansas Paleont. Contrib., Vert., art. 3, p. 121; ETHINGTON AND FURNISH, 1962, Jour. Paleontology, v. 36, p. 1272–1273, Pl. 173, fig. 9; ETHINGTON, 1965, Jour. Paleontology, v. 39, p. 576, Pl. 67, fig. 4

*Lonchodina separata* BRANSON AND MEHL, 1934a, Univ. Missouri Studies, v. 8, p. 211, Pl. 15, fig. 14; FAY, 1952, Univ. Kansas Paleont. Contrib., Vert., art. 3, p. 123

*Lonchodina pulchra* BRANSON AND MEHL, 1934a, Univ. Missouri Studies, v. 8, p. 211, Pl. 15, fig. 16; FAY, 1952, Univ. Kansas Paleont. Contrib., Vert., art. 3, p. 123; BISCHOFF AND ZIEGLER, 1956, Hess. Landesamt Boden., Notizbl., Bd. 84, p. 150; ZIEGLER, 1958, Hess. Landesamt Boden., Notizbl., Bd. 87, p. 12, 21, 29, 32

*Prioniodina curvata* BRANSON AND MEHL, 1934a, Univ. Missouri Studies, v. 8, p. 214, Pl. 14, fig. 17; BRANSON, 1944, Univ. Missouri Studies, v. 19, no. 3, p. 166

*Lonchodina* cf. *L. separata* BRANSON AND MEHL, 1934b, Univ. Missouri Studies, v. 8, p. 291–292, Pl. 23, fig. 22; BRANSON, 1944, Univ. Missouri Studies, v. 19, no. 3, p. 221

*Lonchodina nitela* HUDDLE, 1934, Bull. Am. Paleontology, v. 21, no. 72, p. 16, 82, Pl. 6, figs. 3–5

*Lonchodina curvata* BISCHOFF AND ZIEGLER, 1956, Hess. Landesamt Boden., Notizbl., Bd. 84, p. 150, Pl. 14, fig. 21; BISCHOFF AND ZIEGLER, 1957, Hess. Landesamt Boden., Abh., no. 22, p. 67, Pl. 10, figs. 10a, 10b; LYS, SERRE, AND DEROO, 1957, Inst. Français Pétrole, Rev., v. 12, p. 802, Pl. 10, fig. 3; ZIEGLER, 1958, Hess. Landesamt Boden., Notizbl., Bd. 87, p. 12, 20, 28, 31

*Lonchodina projecta* ETHINGTON, 1962, New Mexico Geol. Soc., Guidebook, 13th Ann. Field Conf., p. 74

REMARKS: There is apparently no significant difference among the specimens described from Europe and North America although several names have been applied.

OCCURRENCE: Middle *dubia* (= *asymmetrica?*) zone, unnamed Upper Devonian formation, Mary's Mountain, Nevada (Fig. 2); 20 specimens

REPOSITORY: USNM 144339

*Lonchodina robusta* Branson and Mehl

(Pl. 5, fig. 4)

*Lonchodina? robusta* BRANSON AND MEHL, 1934a, Univ. Missouri Studies, v. 8, p. 213, Pl. 15, fig. 19; FAY, 1952, Univ. Kansas Paleont. Contrib., Vert., art. 3, p. 123

*Lonchodina multidens* HELMS, 1959, Geologie, v. 8, no. 6, p. 643, Pl. 1, fig. 14, Pl. 4, fig. 15

*Lonchodina robusta* ETHINGTON, 1962, New Mexico Geol. Soc., Guidebook, 13th Ann. Field Conf., p. 74; ETHINGTON AND FURNISH, 1962, Jour. Paleontology, v. 36, p. 1273; ETHINGTON, 1965, Jour. Paleontology, v. 39, p. 576

REMARKS: Fusion of the denticles is less developed on the Utah material than on the types, but, owing to the great variability of this character on other species, this variability is believed to fall within the limits of the species.

OCCURRENCE: Lower and upper *gigas* zones, Pilot Shale; sample 12 collected 0.6 mile southwest of section B and sample 15 collected 1½ miles southwest of section B, Confusion Range, western Utah (Fig. 7); 4 specimens

REPOSITORY: USNM 144340

*Lonchodina typicalis* Bassler

(Pl. 5, fig. 13)

*Lonchodina typicalis* BASSLER, 1925, Geol. Soc. America Bull., v. 36, p. 219; FAY, 1952, Univ. Kansas Paleont. Contrib., Vert., art. 3, p. 124

*Lonchodina subrecta* ULRICH AND BASSLER, 1926, U. S. National Museum, Proc., v. 68, art. 12, p. 33, Pl. 5, figs. 4, 5; FAY, 1952, Univ. Kansas Paleont. Contrib., Vert., art. 3, p. 124

*Lonchodina delicatula* ULRICH AND BASSLER, 1926, U. S. National Museum, Proc., v. 68, art. 12, p. 33, Pl. 5, fig. 11; FAY, 1952, Univ. Kansas Paleont. Contrib., Vert., art. 3, p. 122

EMENDED DESCRIPTION: Arched twisted bar with unequally developed limbs. Apical denticle circular in section whereas others are laterally compressed with sharp edges. Denticles of both limbs are discrete and increase in size toward the distal extremities with those of one limb double the size of the teeth of the other. Aboral edge sharp beneath limbs, blunt below apical denticle. No basal excavation. Swelling at base of apical denticle on concave face of unit continues as narrow shoulder below other teeth.

OCCURRENCE: Middle *Palmatolepis triangularis* zone, Devils Gate Limestone; sample collected 97 feet above sample F-5, Devils Gate Pass, Nevada (Fig. 3); 5 specimens

REPOSITORY: USNM 144342

*Lonchodina* sp. aff. *L. arcuata* Ulrich and Bassler
(Pl. 5, fig. 9)

EMENDED DESCRIPTION: Asymmetrical arched units which are bowed laterally so that the two limbs intersect at an angle of about 135 degrees in both lateral and oral views. Denticles of one limb are discrete, sharp-edged with convex lateral faces, and somewhat variable in size. Teeth of the other limb are closely set and somewhat recurved. The largest tooth is located above the juncture of the two limbs although it is not markedly different from the others. Aboral edge is sharp beneath both limbs but flatter near their juncture where a shallow cavity may be present.

OCCURRENCE: Upper *Palmatolepis triangularis* zone, Pilot Shale; sample 11 from 0.6 mile southwest of section C, Confusion Range, western Utah (Fig. 7); 3 specimens

REPOSITORY: USNM 144343

*Lonchodina* sp.
(Pl. 5, fig. 3)

A single well-preserved specimen, apparently representing a mature stage of development, shows characteristics not recognized on other species. It is arched with limbs at an angle of 180 degrees. Oral surface is expanded and flat with greatest width at the top of the arch and becoming increasingly narrow toward either end. Denticles have convex lateral faces with sharp anterior and posterior edges and are basally crowded but discrete. Teeth of anterior bar about twice the size of those of the other limb. Apical denticle three to four times as long as others and in line with teeth of anterior limb. Denticles of posterior limb are not aligned with teeth of anterior limb or apical denticle. Bar is shallow. Aboral surface obscured by basal attached structure but appears to be flat with a median longitudinal keel.

OCCURRENCE: Middle *Palmatolepis triangularis* zone, Pilot Shale; sample 21 collected 3½ miles southwest of section C, Confusion Range, western Utah (Fig. 7); one specimen

REPOSITORY: USNM 144344

Genus *Neoprioniodus* Rhodes and Müller, 1956
Type species: *Prioniodus conjunctus* Gunnell, 1933
*Neoprioniodus abnormalis* (Stauffer)
(Pl. 6, fig. 12)

*Hindeodelloides abnormale* STAUFFER, 1938, Jour. Paleontology, v. 12, p. 429, Pl. 51, fig. 25; FAY, 1952, Univ. Kansas Paleont. Contrib., Vert., art. 3, p. 108

*?Palmatodella delicatula* HELMS, 1959, Geologie, v. 8, Pl. 3, fig. 13, Pl. 5, fig. 21 (not Pl. 1, fig. 11, Pl. 2, figs. 21, 22, Pl. 3, fig. 15, Pl. 5, figs. 11, 12)

REMARKS: Curvature of the anterior end of the bar is somewhat less than the right angle which Stauffer observed on the holotype. However, this is a feature that is subject to considerable variation in other species and is not specifically diagnostic. In other respects the material conforms rather closely to the characters of the type. Helms (1959) illustrated but did not describe a number of specimens which he referred to *Palmatodella delicatula* Bassler. This species is defined as having hairlike or needlelike denticles, whereas the forms figured by Helms have fairly broad teeth which more nearly conform to *Neoprioniodus* species.

OCCURRENCE:    Upper *Palmatolepis triangularis* zone, Pilot Shale; sample 3 from 0.8 mile north-east of section B, Confusion Range, western Utah (Fig. 7); 5 specimens
REPOSITORY:    USNM 144345

### *Neoprioniodus armatus* (Hinde)
### (Pl. 6, figs. 6, 13)

*Prioniodus armatus* HINDE, 1879, Geol. Soc. London Quart. Jour., v. 35, p. 360, Pl. 15, figs. 20, 21; FAY, 1952, Univ. Kansas Paleont. Contrib., Vert., art. 3, p. 168
*Prioniodus undosus* ULRICH AND BASSLER, 1926, U. S. National Museum, Proc., v. 68, art. 12, p. 12, Pl. 1, figs. 18, 20; FAY, 1952, Univ. Kansas Paleont. Contrib., Vert., art. 3, p. 176
*Prioniodus semiseparatus* BRANSON AND MEHL, 1934a, Univ. Missouri Studies, v. 8, p. 206, Pl. 15, figs. 9, 10; FAY, 1952, Univ. Kansas Paleont. Contrib., Vert., art. 3, p. 175
*Prioniodina armata* SANNEMANN, 1955a, Senckenbergiana Lethaea, Bd. 36, p. 151, Pl. 3, figs. 2, 3; BISCHOFF, 1956, Hess. Landesamt Boden., Notizbl., Bd. 84, p. 116, 117, 135, Pl. 10, figs. 15–17; BISCHOFF AND ZIEGLER, 1956, Hess. Landesamt Boden., Notizbl., Bd. 84, p. 160; BISCHOFF AND ZIEGLER, 1957, Hess. Landesamt Boden., Abh., no. 22, p. 37, 38, 105, Pl. 9, figs. 4a, 4b, 6a, 6b, 9; FLÜGEL AND ZIEGLER, 1957, Naturw. Ver. Steiermark, Mitt., Bd. 87, Table 1; ZIEGLER, 1958, Hess. Landesamt Boden., Notizbl., Bd. 87, p. 13, 21, 29, 32; STOPPEL, 1958, Hess. Landesamt Boden., Notizbl., Bd. 87, p. 96, 98, 99, 100, 101, 102, 105, 112; SCHRIEL AND STOPPEL, 1958b, Deutsch. Geol. Gesell. Zeit., Bd. 110, p. 266; KREBS, 1959, Senckenbergiana Lethaea, Bd. 40, p. 375; SERRE AND LYS, 1960, 21st Internat. Geol. Cong., Rept., pt. 6, p. 38
*Neoprioniodus armatus* HELMS, 1958, Geologie, v. 8, no. 6, p. 644, Pl. 4, fig. 18; ETHINGTON AND FURNISH, 1962, Jour. Paleontology, v. 36, p. 1274–1275
REMARKS:    Different fragments of this form were found in the Devonian of the western facies rocks. European reports have indicated that the species ranged throughout the Upper Devonian.
OCCURRENCE:    Middle *dubia* (= *asymmetrica?*) zone, unnamed Upper Devonian formation, Mary's Mountain, Nevada (Fig. 2); 5 specimens
REPOSITORY:    USNM 144346, 144347

### *Neoprioniodus powellensis* (Stauffer)
### (Pl. 6, fig. 15)

*Prioniodus powellensis* STAUFFER, 1938, Jour. Paleontology, v. 12, p. 441, Pl. 50, fig. 29; FAY, 1952, Univ. Kansas Paleont. Contrib., Vert., art. 3, p. 174
*Prioniodus smithi* STAUFFER, 1938, Jour. Paleontology, v. 12, p. 441, Pl. 50, figs. 26a, 26b; FAY, 1952, Univ. Kansas Paleont. Contrib., Vert., art. 3, p. 175
*Euprioniodina parvula* MILLER AND YOUNGQUIST, 1947, Jour. Paleontology, v. 21, p. 507–508, Pl. 73, fig. 16; FAY, 1952, Univ. Kansas Paleont. Contrib., Vert., art. 3, p. 93
*Prioniodina smithi* SANNEMANN, 1955a, Senckenbergiana Lethaea, Bd. 36, p. 152, Pl. 3, figs. 15, 17; BISCHOFF, 1956, Hess. Landesamt Boden., Notizbl., Bd. 84, p. 116, 117, 135, Pl. 10, figs. 18, 19; BISCHOFF AND ZIEGLER, 1956, Hess. Landesamt Boden., Notizbl., Bd. 84, p. 161; LYS, SERRE, AND DEROO, 1957, Inst. Français Pétrole, Rev., v. 12, p. 806, Pl. 12, fig. 4; p. 1050, Pl. 6, fig. 5; SCHRIEL AND STOPPEL, 1958a, Deutsch. Geol. Gesell. Zeit., Bd. 109, p. 562; ZIEGLER, 1958, Hess. Landesamt Boden., Notizbl., Bd. 87, p. 13, 21, 29, 32, 76; STOPPLE, 1958, Hess. Landesamt Boden., Notizbl., Bd. 87, p. 94, 96, 98, 99, 101, 104, 105, 107, 112, 113; SCHRIEL AND STOPPEL, 1958b, Deutsch. Geol. Gesell. Zeit., Bd. 110, p. 266; HELMS, 1959, Geologie, v. 8, no. 6, p. 653–654, 664, Pl. 1, fig. 15, Pl. 2, fig. 8, Pl. 4, fig. 17; SCHRIEL AND STOPPEL, 1960, Deutsch. Geol. Gesell. Zeit., Bd. 111, p. 668, 669, 670, 675, 676; SERRE AND LYS, 1960, 21st Internat. Geol. Cong., Rept., pt. 6, p. 38; FREYER, 1961, Freiberger Forschungs., v. C95, p. 79, Pl. 5, figs. 118–120; SPASSOV AND STEVANOVIĆ, 1962, Annales Géol. Péninsule Balkanique, v. 29, p. 62, Pl. 2, fig. 12; SPASSOV, 1965, Trav. Géol. Bulgarie, sér. Paléont., v. 7, p. 98, Pl. 3, fig. 7; GLENISTER AND KLAPPER, 1966, Jour. Paleontology, v. 40, p. 833, Pl. 96, figs. 7–9
*Prioniodina powellensis* ETHINGTON AND FURNISH, 1962, Jour. Paleontology, v. 36, p. 1284

REMARKS:  Although *N. powellensis* has been widely reported from Europe where it ranges throughout the entire Upper Devonian section, it is previously known in North America only from the Olentangy and Sweetland Creek shales.

OCCURRENCE:  Middle *Palmatolepis triangularis* zone, Pilot Shale; sample 21 from 3½ miles southwest of section C, Confusion Range, western Utah (Fig. 7); 2 specimens

REPOSITORY:  USNM 144348

### *Neoprioniodus* spp.
### (Pl. 6, fig. 24)

REMARKS:  Typical neoprioniodids appear to be less numerous in the Great Basin Upper Devonian than in correlative strata of Europe and eastern United States. Several unidentified pieces of several different species have been found in a single sample from western Utah.

OCCURRENCE:  Lower *crepida* zone, Pilot Shale; sample C-19 of section C, Confusion Range, western Utah (Fig. 5); 3 specimens

REPOSITORY:  USNM 144349

### Genus *Nothognathella* Branson and Mehl, 1934
### Type species: *N. typicalis* Branson and Mehl, 1934

Restricted to Upper Devonian rocks, species of this genus may have considerab le index value. The small lateral platforms distinguish the species from closely related blades. Six species have been found in the Great Basin rocks.

### *Nothognathella abnormis* Branson and Mehl
### (Pl. 6, fig. 17)

*Nothognathella* (?) *abnormis* BRANSON AND MEHL, 1934a, Univ. Missouri Studies, v. 8, p. 231–232, Pl. 14, figs. 1, 2; FAY, 1952, Univ. Kansas Paleont. Contrib., Vert., art. 3, p. 133; LYS AND SERRE, 1957a, Inst. Français Pétrole, Rev., v. 12, p. 1047, Pl. 4, figs. 6a, 6b; HELMS, 1959, Geologie, v. 8, no. 6, p. 663, Pl. 4, figs. 5, 6
*Nothognathella abnormis* SANNEMANN, 1955a, Senckenbergiana Lethaea, Bd. 36, p. 132, Pl. 6, figs. 16, 17; BISCHOFF, 1956, Hess. Landesamt Boden., Notizbl., Bd. 84, p. 116, 117, 126; BISCHOFF AND ZIEGLER, 1956, Hess. Landesamt Boden., Notizbl., Bd. 84, p. 151; FLÜGEL AND ZIEGLER, 1957, Naturw. Ver. Steiermark, Mitt., Bd. 87, Table 1; ZIEGLER, 1958, Hess. Landesamt Boden., Notizbl., Bd. 87, p. 12, 21, 29, 32, 75; STOPPEL, 1958, Hess. Landesamt Boden., Notizbl., Bd. 87, p. 95, 99, 101, 105; SERRE AND LYS, 1960, 21st Internat. Geol. Cong., Rept., pt. 6, p. 38; CLARK AND BECKER, 1960, Geol. Soc. America Bull., v. 71, p. 1670

REDESCRIPTION:  Arched, bladelike dental units. The anterior limb is straight whereas the shorter posterior limb is turned inward at an angle of 120 degrees and slightly twisted. Approximately 14 fused teeth of the anterior limb increase regularly in length toward the crest of the arch so that their sharp free tips lie along a smooth arc. Eight teeth of the posterior limb are fused throughout most of their length; all are of about the same size, although much shorter than the denticles at the crest of the arch. An aboral keel extends the entire length of the conodont. No escutcheon is present but the keel exhibits a sinuous bend beneath the center of the unit. The convex outer face is smooth except for a protuberance at the base of the first tooth of the posterior limb which is also the point of inflection for the unit. A ridge on the inner face extends the entire length. It widens somewhat from the posterior tip to the mid-point to form a narrow posterior platform which is ornamented along its edge by a series of low nodes. The nodes continue across the anterior limb, becoming increasingly indistinct toward the end.

REMARKS:  Branson and Mehl described a small subapical pit on the type specimens from Missouri. In all other respects the Utah material conforms to the original description. The magnitude of curvature is less than is reported by Sannemann (1955a), although that writer noted that his specimens showed some variation in this respect.

OCCURRENCE:  In Europe this species has been reported from Upper Devonian strata ranging from highest *Manticoceras* strata to *Platyclymenia* strata. Previously recorded North American occurrences include the Saverton Formation of northeastern Missouri and the Sweetland Creek

Shale of eastern Iowa. Lower *gigas* zone, Pilot Shale; sample 12 from 0.6 mile southwest of section B, Confusion Range, western Utah (Fig. 7); 5 specimens

REPOSITORY: USNM 144350

## *Nothognathella angusta* Stauffer
(Pl. 6, fig. 11)

*Nothognathella angusta* STAUFFER, 1938, Jour. Paleontology, v. 12, p. 435–436, Pl. 48, fig. 34; FAY, 1952, Univ. Kansas Paleont. Contrib., Vert., art. 3, p. 133; BISCHOFF AND ZIEGLER, 1957, Hess. Landesamt Boden., Abh., no. 22, p. 37, 38, 39, 73, 131; BISCHOFF AND SANNEMANN, 1958, Hess. Landesamt Boden., Notizbl., Bd. 86, p. 91, 98; ZIEGLER, 1958, Hess. Landesamt Boden., Notizbl., Bd. 87, p. 12, 21, 29, 32, 75

*Nothognathella bogartensis* STAUFFER, 1938, Jour. Paleontology, v. 12, p. 436, Pl. 40, fig. 30; FAY, 1952, Univ. Kansas Paleont. Contrib., Vert., art. 3, p. 133

*Nothognathella* cf. *angusta* LYS, SERRE, AND DEROO, 1957, Inst. Français Pétrole, Rev., v. 12, p. 802–803, Pl. 10, fig. 4

REDESCRIPTION: Slightly arched units which are somewhat bowed laterally and twisted at the top of the arch so that the two limbs are not in the same plane. Denticles of the posterior limb are circular in cross section, erect, and fused throughout their length. They follow a sinuous curve near the highest part of the unit but are arranged in a nearly straight line toward the anterior tip. Teeth of the posterior limb are only half as high as those of the anterior limb and no transitional denticles are present so that the contrast in length is pronounced. The aboral surface is broad with a median keel which becomes increasingly sharp and prominent toward either end. A thin groove ending in a tiny subapical pit may be present on the keel. Flanges on either side of the unit are broadest near mid-length, becoming progressively narrow toward the distal ends of the limbs. The outer flange attains its greatest width just posterior to the point of maximum lateral curvature of the conodont, whereas the inner flange is widest at or immediately anterior to this point. Both are ornamented by low nodes which may be aligned in rows normal to the edges of the flanges.

REMARKS: This species is close to *Nothognathella brevidonta* Youngquist. The principal differences are the absence of any type of basal excavation in the latter species and the apparently weaker development of the keel in *N. angusta*. The subapical pit was not present on all the specimens studied and was extremely small wherever observed. In other respects the two species are nearly identical and they may well prove to be conspecific.

OCCURRENCE: European workers have found *N. angusta* in lower Upper Devonian strata and in North America it has been reported only from the Olentangy Shale. Lower *gigas* zone, Pilot Shale; figured specimen from sample 12 which was obtained 0.6 mile southwest of section B, Confusion Range, western Utah (Fig. 7). Also occurs through the *rhomboidea* zone of the Devils Gate Limestone, sample E-1, Diamond Range, Nevada (Fig. 4); 10 specimens

REPOSITORY: USNM 144351

## *Nothognathella condita* Branson and Mehl
(Pl. 7, fig. 4)

*Nothognathella condita* BRANSON AND MEHL, 1934a, Univ. Missouri Studies, v. 8, p. 230, Pl. 13, figs. 25–26; FAY, 1952, Univ. Kansas Paleont. Contrib., Vert., art. 3, p. 133; SANNEMANN, 1955a, Senckenbergiana Lethaea, Bd. 36, p. 132, Pl. 3, figs. 9a, 9b; STOPPEL, 1958, Hess. Landesamt Boden., Notizbl., Bd. 87, p. 105

*Nothognathella delawarensis* CLARK AND BECKER, 1960, Geol. Soc. America Bull., v. 71, p. 1670

NEW DESCRIPTION: The two limbs, which are almost equal in length, form an angle of 150 degrees. Anterior limb is straight; posterior limb slightly offset and twisted, particularly near the distal end. Denticles on the anterior limb are laterally compressed, increase in height posteriorly, and are completely fused to form a fan-shaped blade. Posterior teeth are very short and peglike, irregularly developed, and tend to be fused. Aboral surface is sharply keeled except beneath the center of the unit where the keel is low and interrupted by a tiny oval escutcheon. A basally attached structure which differs in color from the conodont may be retained along the sharp edge of the keel throughout its entire length. Flanges extend along both sides of the unit at about mid-height. The outer one is narrow but reaches its greatest width at the crest of the arch. Low nodes are present but become indistinct toward either end. The inner flange forms a shelf on the inner side of the posterior limb which is only slightly broader at mid-length than distally. Anteriorly it is reduced to a narrow ridge. Nodes and bars on the posterior shelf are arranged at a high angle to the periphery.

REMARKS: Both the type specimens from the Saverton Formation of Missouri and the material illustrated by Sannemann show equal development of the flanges on either side of the posterior limb. The ornamentation of the previously described specimens is more robust than in the material from the Great Basin. The similarity of the denticulation and development of the keel is in close agreement in each case and suggests that all are conspecific.

OCCURRENCE: *N. condita* is known in Europe from strata of the *Cheiloceras* and lower *Platyclymenia* zones. It has been reported only from the Saverton Formation of Missouri prior to the present study. Upper *Palmatolepis triangularis* zone, Pilot Shale; sample 11 from 0.6 mile southwest of section C, Confusion Range, western Utah (Fig. 7); 3 specimens

REPOSITORY: USNM 144352

### *Nothognathella incurva* Branson and Mehl
(Pl. 6, fig. 18)

*Nothognathella incurva* BRANSON AND MEHL, 1934a, Univ. Missouri Studies, v. 8, p. 228, Pl. 13, figs. 13, 14; FAY, 1952, Univ. Kansas Paleont. Contrib., Vert., art. 3, p. 133

REDESCRIPTION: The two subequal limbs meet at an angle of 150 degrees with the posterior limb slightly offset so that, in oral view, the unit has a sinuous curve near the middle. Teeth of the anterior limb are subequal in length and almost completely fused. Posterior teeth are much shorter, conical in shape, and closely set although not fused. The unit is aborally keeled throughout its length except for a moderately large but very shallow medial escutcheon. The inner lateral flange is broad from the posterior tip to the point of curvature between the two limbs and continues anteriorly as a narrow shoulder. The oral surface is ornamented by small papillae with a series of inconspicuous nodes along the periphery. On the outer face a narrow flange extends from the posterior end past mid-length, then becomes increasingly narrow anteriorly.

OCCURRENCE: The species has not been reported from Europe. Other North American occurrences are in the Saverton Formation and the Sylamore Sandstone. Lower *crepida* zone, Pilot Shale; Sample C-19 of section C, Confusion Range, western Utah (Fig. 5); 4 specimens

REPOSITORY: USNM 144353

### *Nothognathella reversa* Branson and Mehl
(Pl. 5, fig. 1; Pl. 6, fig. 19)

*Nothognathella reversa* BRANSON AND MEHL, 1934a, Univ. Missouri Studies, v. 8, p. 231, Pl. 13, figs. 9, 10; FAY, 1952, Univ. Kansas Paleont. Contrib., Vert., art. 3, p. 133

REDESCRIPTION: Arched units with subequal limbs forming an angle of about 150 degrees. The anterior limb is straight and bears erect fused teeth which increase slightly in length toward the center of the unit. Posterior limb is continuously curved laterally along its length and twisted at the distal end. Posterior denticles are low, fused, and somewhat irregular in their development. Aborally, the unit bears a sharp keel except for an elliptical escutcheon at the crest of the arch. An inner lateral flange widens from the posterior tip to beyond mid-length, but narrows rapidly before continuing as a narrow shoulder to the anterior end. A corresponding outer flange remains narrow except for a small local expansion posterior to the middle of the unit. The flanges on most specimens are unornamented although a few specimens display peripheral nodes.

REMARKS: A single gerontic specimen shows the posterior denticles so completely fused that their identity is lost except at the sharp tips. The resultant structure resembles a fan with a serrate edge.

OCCURRENCE: The species has been reported previously only from the Saverton Formation of northeastern Missouri. Middle and upper *Palmatolepis triangularis* zones and lower *crepida* zone.

Pilot Shale; from samples 21, 11, and C-19 of section C, Confusion Range, western Utah (Figs. 5 and 7); 8 specimens

REPOSITORY:   USNM 144354; UW 1003

Genus *Ozarkodina* Branson and Mehl, 1933
Type species: *O. typica* Branson and Mehl, 1933
*Ozarkodina immersa* (Hinde)
(Pl. 6, fig. 10)

*Polygnathus immersus* HINDE, 1879, Geol. Soc. London Quart. Jour., v. 35, p. 364, Pl. 16, fig. 21
*Bryantodus immersus* BRANSON AND MEHL, 1934a, Univ. Missouri Studies, v. 8, p. 140, Pl. 11, fig. 22
*Ctenognathus elegans* STAUFFER, 1938, Jour. Paleontology, v. 12, p. 424–425, Pl. 48, figs. 9, 12; FAY, 1952, Univ. Kansas Paleont. Contrib., Vert., art. 3, p. 84
*Ctenognathus falcatus* STAUFFER, 1938, Jour. Paleontology, v. 12, p. 425, Pl. 48, figs. 1, 5; FAY, 1952, Univ. Kansas Paleont. Contrib., Vert., art. 3, p. 84
*Ctenognathus falsiformis* STAUFFER, 1938, Jour. Paleontology, v. 12, p. 425, Pl. 48, figs. 4, 7; FAY, 1952, Univ. Kansas Paleont. Contrib., Vert., art. 3, p. 84
*Ctenognathus firmus* STAUFFER, 1938, Jour. Paleontology, v. 12, p. 425, Pl. 48, figs. 2, 6, 15
*Ozarkodina elegans* SANNEMANN, 1955a, Senckenbergiana Lethaea, Bd. 36, Pl. 6, fig. 9; BISCHOFF AND ZIEGLER, 1957, Hess. Landesamt Boden., Abh., no. 22, p. 31–39, 76, Pl. 20, figs. 29–33; STOPPEL, 1958, Hess. Landesamt Boden., Notizbl., Bd. 87, p. 101, 105, 113; ZIEGLER, 1958, Hess. Landesamt Boden., Notizbl., Bd. 87, p. 13, 21, 29, 32, 75; SCHRIEL AND STOPPEL, 1958b, Deutsch. Geol. Gesell. Zeit., Bd. 110, p. 274; KREBS, 1959, Senckenbergiana Lethaea, Bd. 40, p. 373, 374, 375; FREYER, 1961, Freiberger Forschungs., v. C95, p. 57–58; ETHINGTON AND FURNISH, 1962, Jour. Paleontology, v. 36, p. 1277–1278; ETHINGTON, 1965, Jour. Paleontology, v. 39, p. 577, Pl. 68, fig. 15

REMARKS:   As has been shown by Sannemann (1955a, p. 133), variations within this species cover a broad range encompassing several forms described by Stauffer. Those represented in the western facies of the Nevada Upper Devonian are somewhat more highly arched than others previously described. However, the lateral curvature of the blade and inclined slender fused denticles serve to identify the species. The more widely used name *Ozarkodina elegans* is clearly a junior synonym.

OCCURRENCE:   This has been reported from strata ranging from highest Middle Devonian through middle Upper Devonian. Middle *dubia* (= *asymmetrica?*) zone, unnamed Upper Devonian formation, Mary's Mountain, Nevada (Fig. 2); 4 specimens

REPOSITORY:   USNM 144355

*Ozarkodina macra* Branson and Mehl
(Pl. 4, fig. 2; Pl. 5, fig. 2)

*Ozarkodina macra* BRANSON AND MEHL, 1934a, Univ. Missouri Studies, v. 8, p. 192, Pl. 17, fig. 5; FAY, 1952, Univ. Kansas Paleont. Contrib., Vert., art. 3, p. 138; BISCHOFF AND ZIEGLER, 1957, Hess. Landesamt Boden., Abh., no. 22, p. 77–78, Pl. 12, figs. 13a, 13b, Pl. 13, figs. 9a, 9b; ZIEGLER, 1958, Hess. Landesamt Boden., Notizbl., Bd. 87, p. 13, 76; ETHINGTON AND FURNISH, 1962, Jour. Paleontology, v. 36, p. 1278; ETHINGTON, 1965, Jour. Paleontology, v. 39, p. 578

REMARKS:   Several mature specimens compare with previously described specimens in curvature and twisting of the posterior part of the blade but are smaller and thinner with fewer denticles. They are probably slightly younger than most forms described. Definite juveniles have also been found.

OCCURRENCE:   Middle *P. triangularis* and lower *crepida* zone, Pilot Shale; from sample 21 and unit C-19 of section C, Confusion Range, western Utah (Fig. 5); 6 specimens

REPOSITORY:   USNM 144356, UW 1004

*Ozarkodina* spp.
(Pl. 6, fig. 9)

REMARKS:   Although *Ozarkodina* ranges throughout the Devonian sections studied, most specimens recovered were fragmental and represented only halves of blades. Such material cannot be identified specifically. Several unbroken specimens in the Great Basin collections are more distinct but are represented by only one or two individuals and do not appear to be identifiable with previously described species. One such individual is figured.

OCCURRENCE: In all zones of Upper Devonian. Figured specimen from unit C-19 of section C, Pilot Shale, Confusion Range, western Utah (Fig. 5); 37 specimens

REPOSITORY: USNM 144357

Genus Palmatolepis Ulrich and Bassler, 1926
Type species: P. perlobata Ulrich and Bassler, 1926

Species of this genus are the best "index fossils" for Upper Devonian rocks and numerous papers have emphasized their value during the last few years. Müller (1956b) published the first monograph concerning the genus and gave range charts. Sannemann (1955a,b) previously had given some stratigraphic data, and more recently Ziegler (1958; 1962a; 1962b) has discussed the evolutionary significance and has indicated their value in Upper Devonian biostratigraphy.

Ziegler (1962a) and most other students of *Palmatolepis* have assumed that *Polygnathus dubia* (= *asymmetrica ovalis?*) is the generalized platform type which well could be the morphologic ancestor of the Late Devonian *Palmatolepis*. Its stratigraphic occurrence and generalized characters add weight to this argument. However, the *dubia* (= *asymmetrica?*) fauna from Nevada contains specimens which suggest an alternate phylogeny for *Palmatolepis*. Specimens described here as *Palmatolepis? ziegleri* n. sp. occur in the lower part of the Great Basin upper Devonian prior to the appearance of any *Palmatolepis* noted to date. All specimens possess a high, denticulated blade and carina and a flattened moderate to narrow nodose platform. Associated with these specimens are species of *Polygnathellus* which have a strongly curved carina and whose outer platform is narrower than that of *Palmatolepis? ziegleri* n. sp. These are the principal differences and *P.? ziegleri* n. sp. appears to be transitional between *Polygnathellus* and true *Palmatolepis* (Pl. 5, fig. 8; Pl. 8, fig. 14). Growth stages of *P.? ziegleri* n. sp. from young through gerontic individuals have been found and the curved carina, which is characteristic of the *Polygnathellus*, does not occur on any.

Specimens described as *Nothognathella sublaevis* by Sannemann (1955a, p. 132–133, Pl. 3, figs. 10, 12) and Bischoff (1956, p. 127, Pl. 10, figs. 30, 31) are similar but have a long free blade and all are strongly arched. None of the growth stages of *P.? ziegleri* show these characteristics.

Only *Palmatolepis martenbergensis* and *P. transitans* occur in rocks older than those in which *P.? ziegleri* n. sp. has been found and these latter species seem to be equally good transitional types from *Polygnathus dubia* (= *asymmetrica ovalis?*) to more advanced *Palmatolepis* species. It may be that *Palmatolepis* is polyphyletic in origin.

Complete synonyms and descriptions for species of *Palmatolepis* are not listed. The original reference is cited and, generally, Ziegler (1962b) or Glenister and Klapper (1966) are also cited because these references include rather complete descriptions and references to the species. Nomenclature and taxonomic revisions by Ziegler (1962b) have also made it necessary to include references to the original work on Great Basin species of *Palmatolepis* (Clark and Becker, 1960).

Palmatolepis coronata Müller
(Pl. 4, figs. 7, 10; Pl. 8, fig. 6)

*Palmatolepis (Deflectolepis) coronata* MÜLLER, 1956b, Senckenbergischen Naturf. Gesell., Abh., Bd. 494, p. 31, Pl. 10, figs. 17, 18; CLARK AND BECKER, 1960, Geol. Soc. America Bull., v. 71, p. 1673, Pl. 1, figs. 1–5, Pl. 2, fig. 11

REMARKS: Specimens figured by Clark and Becker (1960, Pl. 1, figs. 1–5, Pl. 2, fig. 11) as *P. coronata* were considered to belong with *P. marginata clarki* by Ziegler (1962b, p. 62). This idea is apparently based on Ziegler's suggestion that *P. marginata clarki* (= *P. delicatula clarki*) can be distinguished from *P. coronata* because the latter species has a blade which is highest somewhat in front of the anterior end and decreases in height after this point. This characteristic was used by Müller (1956b, p. 31) in defining *P. coronata*. If this idea is valid then the specimens previously figured from the Great Basin rocks as *P. coronata* = *P. marginata clarki*. However, other material in the Great Basin collections which is otherwise identical with those specimens originally figured have a *P. coronata* type blade (Pl. 8, fig. 6). This suggests that the definitions of *P. coronata* and *P. marginata clarki* are not distinct and that the characteristics are transitional. Perhaps *P. marginata clarki* could be considered a junior synonym of *P. coronata* but, because the stratigraphic range of *P. coronata sensu stricto* may be different from that of *P. marginata clarki sensu stricto*, the forms are best treated as separate species at present.

OCCURRENCE: Middle *P. triangularis* and lower *crepida* zone, Pilot Shale; from sample 21 and unit C-19, Confusion Range, western Utah (Fig. 5); more than 50 specimens

REPOSITORY: USNM 144358, BYU 525–528, UW 1007

### *Palmatolepis crepida* Sannemann
#### (Pl. 4, fig. 17)

*Palmatolepis crepida* SANNEMANN, 1955a, Senckenbergiana Lethaea, Bd. 36, p. 123, Pl. 6, fig. 21; ZIEGLER, 1962b, Hess. Landesamt Boden., Abh., no. 38, p. 55, Pl. 6, figs. 12–19; BOUCKAERT AND ZIEGLER, 1965, Mém. Expl. Cartes Géol. Minières Belgique, Mem. 5, Pl. 2, fig. 1–3

*Palmatolepis (Palmatolepis)* sp. aff. *crepida* CLARK AND BECKER, 1960, Geol. Soc. America Bull., v. 71, p. 1671, Pl. 2, figs. 9, 10 (not figs. 3–5)

REMARKS: A subspecies was designated by Ziegler (1962b, p. 55) in order to include the elongate *P. linguiformis;* recent work has indicated that this is not necessary (Glenister and Klapper, 1966, p. 784–785).

OCCURRENCE: *Rhomboidea* zone, uppermost Devils Gate Limestone; sample E-1 of section E, Diamond Range, Nevada (Fig. 4); 4 specimens

REPOSITORY: BYU 516

### *Palmatolepis delicatula delicatula* Branson and Mehl
#### (Pl. 4, fig. 12)

*Palmatolepis delicatula* BRANSON AND MEHL, 1934b, Univ. Missouri Studies, v. 8, p. 227, Pl. 18, figs. 4, 10

*Palmatolepis marginatus* STAUFFER, 1938, Jour. Paleontology, v. 12, p. 437, Pl. 53, figs. 3, 7, 8, 13, 17 (in part)

*Palmatolepis (Manticolepis) marginata* var. A CLARK AND BECKER, 1960, Geol. Soc. America Bull. v. 71, p. 1672, Pl. 1, figs. 9, 10, 11

*Palmatolepis marginata marginata* ZIEGLER, 1962b, Hess. Landesamt Boden., Abh., no. 38, p. 61–62, Pl. 2, figs. 13–19, Fig. 4

*Palmatolepis delicatula delicatula* BOUCKAERT AND ZIEGLER, 1965, Mém. Expl. Cartes Géol. Minières Belgique, Mem. 5, Pl. 2, fig. 9; GLENISTER AND KLAPPER, 1966, Jour. Paleontology, v. 40, p. 807–808, Pl. 95, fig. 17

REMARKS: This species is distinguished from the closely similar *P. delicatula clarki* by the large-sized platform and small free blade. Transitional types are common.

OCCURRENCE: Middle and upper *Palmatolepis triangularis* zones; Devils Gate Formation and Pilot Shale; sample collected 97 feet above F-5 of section F, Devils Gate Pass, Nevada (Fig. 3); sample 3, 0.8 mile northeast of section B and sample 21, 3½ miles southwest of section C, Confusion Range, western Utah (Fig. 7); more than 100 specimens

REPOSITORY: USNM 144361

### *Palmatolepis delicatula clarki* Ziegler
#### (Pl. 4, figs. 9, 14)

*Palmatolepis (Manticolepis) marginata* var. B CLARK AND BECKER, 1960, Geol. Soc. America Bull. v. 71, p. 1672–1673, Pl. 2, figs. 11, 12, 13

*Palmatolepis marginata clarki* ZIEGLER, 1962b, Hess. Landesamt Boden., Abh., no. 38, p. 62–65, Pl. 2, figs. 20–27, Fig. 4

*Palmatolepis delicatula clarki* BOUCKAERT AND ZIEGLER, 1965, Mém. Expl. Cartes Géol. Minières Belgique, Mem. 5, Pl. 2, fig. 4; GLENISTER AND KLAPPER, 1966, Jour. Paleontology, v. 40, p. 808, Pl. 92, fig. 12

REMARKS: The similarity and transitional types with *P. coronata* have been discussed under the *P. coronata* section. The reduced platform and nodose margin distinguish this form from *P. delicatula delicatula.* The interesting history of the name has been treated by Glenister and Klapper

(1966, p. 807). Study of the type material at the University of Missouri has confirmed the fact that *P. marginata* is most likely a junior synonym of *P. delicatula*.

OCCURRENCE: Middle and upper *Palmatolepis triangularis* zones, Pilot Shale; sample 3 (upper), 0.8 mile northeast of section B and sample 21 (middle), 3½ miles southwest of section C, Confusion Range, western Utah (Fig. 7); more than 100 specimens

REPOSITORY: USNM 144359, 144360

### *Palmatolepis foliacea* Youngquist
### (Pl. 8, figs. 3, 14)

*Palmatolepis foliaceus* YOUNGQUIST, 1945, Jour. Paleontology, v. 19, p. 364, Pl. 56, figs. 11, 12
*Palmatolepis foliacea* GLENISTER AND KLAPPER, 1966, Jour. Paleontology, v. 40, p. 810

REMARKS: This species is abundant but specimens are poorly preserved in the Great Basin material. Anterior part of the platform on either side of the carina is commonly bowed upward and nodose ornamentation may be concentrated on margins of platform, especially the inner. Free blade is short and carina is slightly curved to principal node where marked offset in alignment of nodes occurs. Platform margins diverge outward from blade and are almost straight for up to half their length.

OCCURRENCE: This species is common in the basal beds of the Pilot Shale, upper beds of the Guilmette Formation, and the middle beds of the Devils Gate Formation. *Ancyrodella triangularis* zone, Devils Gate Formation; sample F-15 of section F, Devils Gate Pass, Nevada (Fig. 3); sample 12, lower *gigas* zone, Pilot Shale, 0.6 mile southwest of section B, Confusion Range, western Utah (Fig. 7); more than 100 specimens

REPOSITORY: UW 1005, 1006

### *Palmatolepis gigas* Miller and Youngquist
### (Pl. 4, fig. 19)

*Palmatolepis gigas* MILLER AND YOUNGQUIST, 1947, Jour. Paleontology, v. 21, p. 512–513, Pl. 75, fig. 1; KLAPPER AND FURNISH, 1963, Iowa Acad. Sci., Proc. 1962, v. 69, p. 406–407
*Palmatolepis rhenana* BISCHOFF, 1956, Hess. Landesamt Boden., Notizbl., Bd. 84, p. 129–130, Pl. 8, figs. 26–28, 30, Pl. 10, fig. 7; ZIEGLER, 1962b, Hess. Landesamt Boden., Abh., no. 38, p. 21–24; KLAPPER AND FURNISH, 1963, Iowa Acad. Sci., Proc. 1962, v. 69, p. 407; GLENISTER AND KLAPPER, 1966, Jour. Paleontology, v. 40, p. 810, Pl. 88, fig. 12

REMARKS: This species is characterized by an extremely large inner lobe. Many specimens in the Utah collections are broken but the easily recognized fragments have allowed widespread identification of the species. *Palmatolepis rhenana* Bischoff was considered distinct from *P. gigas* by European students and in the original zonation of Ziegler (1962b) a zone of *P. rhenana* was recognized. More recently, Klapper and Furnish (1963, p. 407) have indicated that *P. rhenana* is a junior synonym of *P. gigas* and that the zone should be renamed. The suggestion is followed here.

OCCURRENCE: Lower through upper *gigas* zone, Devils Gate Formation and Pilot Shale; sample 2, 0.5 mile northeast of section B; sample 12, 0.6 mile southwest of section B, Confusion Range, western Utah (Fig. 7); more than 100 specimens

REPOSITORY: USNM 144365

### *Palmatolepis glabra glabra* Ulrich and Bassler
### (Pl. 9, fig. 8)

*Palmatolepis glabra* ULRICH AND BASSLER, 1926, U. S. National Museum, Proc., v. 68, no. 2613, p. 51, Pl. 8, figs. 18–20
*Palmatolepis glabra glabra* ZIEGLER, 1962b, Hess. Landesamt Boden., Abh., no. 38, p. 58, Pl. 4, figs. 14, 15; GLENISTER AND KLAPPER, 1966, Jour. Paleontology, v. 40, p. 811, Pl. 89, figs. 6, 7, Pl. 90, fig. 3

REMARKS: In his revision of certain species of *Palmatolepis*, Ziegler (1962b) recognized several distinct forms of *P. glabra*. In the Great Basin material all the variants occur together whereas the German section contains different forms at various intervals. Some mixing may have occurred but this is difficult to substantiate.

OCCURRENCE: *Rhomboidea* zone, uppermost Devils Gate Formation; sample E-1 of section E, Diamond Range, Nevada (Fig. 4); 15 specimens

REPOSITORY: BYU 521

### *Palmatolepis glabra elongata* Holmes

*Palmatolepis elongata* HOLMES, 1928, U. S. National Museum, Proc., v. 72, no. 2701, p. 33, Pl. 11, fig. 33

*Palmatolepis glabra elongata* ZIEGLER, 1962b, Hess. Landesamt Boden., Abh., no. 38, p. 58, Pl. 5, figs. 6, 7; GLENISTER AND KLAPPER, 1966, Jour. Paleontology, v. 40, p. 813–814, Pl. 95, fig. 1

REMARKS: This species is not figured here because all specimens in the Nevada collections are broken and not well preserved. Ziegler (1962b, Pl. 5, figs. 6, 7) illustrated two varieties of this species which are evidently the same as those from the Devils Gate Formation.

OCCURRENCE: *Rhomboidea* zone, uppermost beds of Devils Gate Formation; sample E-1 of section E, Diamond Range, Nevada (Fig. 4); 5 specimens

### *Palmatolepis glabra pectinata* Ziegler
(Pl. 4, fig. 8)

*Palmatolepis glabra pectinata* ZIEGLER, 1960b, Fortschr. Geol. Rheinld. u. Westf., v. 6, p. 8–9, Pl. 21, figs. 3–5; ZIEGLER, 1962b, Hess. Landesamt Boden., Abh., no. 38, p. 59, Pl. 4, fig. 16, Pl. 5, figs. 3, 5; GLENISTER AND KLAPPER, 1966, Jour. Paleontology, v. 40, p. 814, Pl. 89, figs. 1–3, 5, 9, 10, Pl. 90, figs. 4, 5, Pl. 91, figs. 1, 3, 5

*Palmatolepis (Palmatolepis) distorta* CLARK AND BECKER, 1960, Geol. Soc. America Bull., v. 71, p. 1669–1670, Pl. 2, fig. 7 (not figs. 6, 8)

REMARKS: *P. glabra pectinata* is distinguished by the short upfolded margin which is parallel to the carina on the outer side. Glenister and Klapper (1966, p. 814) have outlined the differences among the *P. glabra* subspecies including the observation that on *P. glabra pectinata*, the upturned margin (parapet) lies closer to the blade and may be longer than that of *P. glabra glabra*. This appears to be a key characteristic for discrimination of the Great Basin species.

OCCURRENCE: *Rhomboidea* zone, uppermost beds of Devils Gate Formation; sample E-1 of section E, Diamond Range, Nevada (Fig. 4); 10 specimens

REPOSITORY: BYU 517

### *Palmatolepis glabra* n. subspecies A Ziegler
(Pl. 4, fig. 18)

*Palmatolepis (Palmatolepis) distorta* CLARK AND BECKER, 1960, Geol. Soc. America Bull., v. 71, p. 1669–1670, Pl. 2, fig. 8 (not figs. 6, 7)

*Palmatolepis glabra* n. subsp. A ZIEGLER, 1962b, Hess. Landesamt Boden., Abh., no. 38, p. 59, Pl. 5, figs. 1, 2

REMARKS: The anteriorly projecting outer platform distinguishes this species. It does not project as strongly as in the specimens figured by Ziegler (1962b) but there is a clear difference between this projection and that of *P. glabra elongata*.

OCCURRENCE: *Rhomboidea* zone, Devils Gate Formation; sample E-1 of section E, Diamond Mountains, Nevada (Fig. 4); 7 specimens

REPOSITORY: BYU 523

### *Palmatolepis hassi* Müller and Müller
(Pl. 8, fig. 13)

*Palmatolepis hassi* MÜLLER AND MÜLLER, 1957, Jour. Paleontology, v. 31, p. 1102–1103, Pl. 139, fig. 2, Pl. 140, figs. 2, 4

REMARKS: This species is quite similar to *P. subrecta* from which it is differentiated by the lack of a secondary carina, a less sigmoidal keel, and by a well-developed inner lobe which is more anterior. It is morphologically the direct ancestor of *P. gigas* (Helms, 1963, fig. 2) which occurs in younger rocks.

OCCURRENCE: Upper *dubia* (=*asymmetrica?*) or lower *A. triangularis* zone, upper beds of Guilmette Formation, Confusion Range, Utah, below section B (Fig. 5); 2 specimens
REPOSITORY: UW 1010

*Palmatolepis linguiformis* Müller
(Pl. 4, fig. 16)

*Palmatolepis (Palmatolepis) linguiformis* MÜLLER, 1956b, Senckenbergischen Naturf. Gesell., Abh., Bd. 494, p. 24, Pl. 7, figs. 1–7; CLARK AND BECKER, 1960, Geol. Soc. America Bull., v. 71, p. 1672, Pl. 1, figs. 14, 15; ? GLENISTER AND KLAPPER, 1966, Jour. Paleontology, v. 40, p. 815–816, Pl. 88, figs. 4, 5

*Palmatolepis crepida linguiformis* ZIEGLER, 1962b, Hess. Landesamt Boden., Abh., no. 38, p. 53–55
REMARKS: This species is abundant in the Pilot Shale but complete specimens are rare. It occurs in an arenaceous limestone and the large-sized individuals have been broken into small but recognizable fragments.

OCCURRENCE: Upper *gigas* zone, Pilot Shale; sample 2 collected half a mile northeast of section B and sample 15 collected 1½ miles southwest of section B, Confusion Range, western Utah (Fig. 7); more than 50 specimens
REPOSITORY: BYU 538

*Palmatolepis minuta* Branson and Mehl
(Pl. 9, fig. 2)

*Palmatolepis minuta* BRANSON AND MEHL, 1934a, Univ. Missouri Studies, v. 8, p. 236, Pl. 18, figs. 1, 6, 7

*Palmatolepis (Deflectolepis) minuta* CLARK AND BECKER, 1960, Geol. Soc. America Bull., v. 71, p. 1673, Pl. 2, fig. 1

*Palmatolepis minuta minuta* ZIEGLER, 1962b, Hess. Landesamt Boden., Abh., no. 38, p. 65–66, Pl. 3, figs. 1–10, Fig. 5; GLENISTER AND KLAPPER, 1966, Jour. Paleontology, v. 40, p. 817, Pl. 90, figs. 1, 2, 7–14

REMARKS: Ziegler (1962b) pointed out that this form, in its earliest stages, is quite similar to *P. marginata marginata*. Some of the material from the Great Basin shows what may be transitional sequences from *P. marginata marginata* through *P. marginata clarki* to *P. minuta*.

OCCURRENCE: Lower *crepida* zone, sample C-19 of section C, Confusion Range, western Utah (Fig. 5); *Rhomboidea* zone, uppermost beds of Devils Gate Formation; sample E-1 of section E, Diamond Range, Nevada (Fig. 4); 15 specimens
REPOSITORY: BYU 518

*Palmatolepis perlobata schindewolfi* Müller
(Pl. 4, fig. 5)

*Palmatolepis (Palmatolepis) schindewolfi* MÜLLER, 1956b, Senckenbergischen Naturf. Gesell., Abh., Bd. 494, p. 27–28, Pl. 8, figs. 22, 23, 25–31, Pl. 9, fig. 33

*Palmatolepis (Palmatolepis) sp. aff. crepida* CLARK AND BECKER, 1960, Geol. Soc. America Bull., v. 71, p. 1671, Pl. 2, fig. 3 (not figs. 4, 5, 9, 10)

*Palmatolepis perlobata schindewolfi* ZIEGLER, 1962b, Hess. Landesamt Boden., Abh., no. 38, p. 70–71, Pl. 8, figs. 2–5

*Palmatolepis perlobata perlobata* GLENISTER AND KLAPPER, 1966, Jour. Paleontology, v. 40, p. 818, Pl. 93, figs. 1, 3, 4, 5, 6

REMARKS: Only a few specimens of this species have been found in a single sample of Pilot Shale. Glenister and Klapper (1966, p. 818) stated that criteria for subspecific differentiation of *P. perlobata perlobata* and *P. perlobata schindewolfi* were " inconsistent within single samples" and that "variable characters include presence or absence of secondary carinae and weak posterior or anterior direction of the inner lobe." For these reasons, the two subspecies were considered synonyms. None of the specimens figured by these writers (Pl. 92, figs. 8, 13; Pl. 93, figs. 1–6) illustrate such variability, however, and this idea will have to be substantiated. Most of their figures seem to conform to the definition of *P. perlobata schindewolfi*.

occurrence: In Europe, this species ranges from the upper *crepida* zone to the lower *costatus* zone.

The sample (22) from the Pilot Shale was collected 3.8 miles southwest of section C and was stratigraphically located about 100 feet above sample C-19 (Fig. 7), here determined to contain the lower *crepida* zone fauna. The general stratigraphic distribution of the conodont zones in the Pilot Shale and the lower limit of the known range of this species in Europe (upper *crepida*) would suggest that the sample from which this species was taken would be at least upper *crepida* and perhaps as high as lower *quadrantinodosa*. The species has not been found in the higher intervals in the Great Basin so that no comparison is possible. On the bases of the stratigraphic position of this sample well above the lower *crepida* zone and the absence of this species in the abundant faunas of the *rhomboidea* and lower *quadrantinodosa* zones of the Great Basin, one might conclude an upper *crepida* age. This, of course, would be a maximum age and the real age is probably no younger than *quadrantinodosa*; 5 specimens

repository: BYU 522

### *Palmatolepis quadrantinodosalobata* Sannemann
(Pl. 9, figs. 1, 4)

*Palmatolepis quadrantinodosalobata* SANNEMANN, 1955b, Neues Jahrbuch Geol. Paläont., Abh., Bd. 100, p. 328, Pl. 24, fig. 6; ZIEGLER, 1962b, Hess. Landesamt Boden., Abh., no. 38, p. 72–73, Pl. 2, figs. 6–12; GLENISTER AND KLAPPER, 1966, Jour. Paleontology, v. 40, p. 821, Pl. 92, figs. 1–3

*Palmatolepis (Manticolepis?) quadrantinodosalobata* CLARK AND BECKER, 1960, Geol. Soc. America Bull., v. 71, p. 1673, Pl. 1, figs. 6–8

remarks: Complete ontogenetic stages have been found in the Utah collections. As indicated by Ziegler (1962b, p. 73), there are apparently an older group of *P. quadrantinodosalobata*, represented by specimens in the middle and upper *P. triangularis* zone, and a younger, more typical of the type group, represented in the *crepida* zone.

occurrence: Middle *Palmatolepis triangularis* zone (transitional types) through lower *crepida* zone, Pilot Shale; sample 11, 0.6 mile southwest of section C; sample 21, 3½ miles southwest of section C; and sample C-19 of section C, Confusion Range, western Utah (Fig. 7); more than 100 specimens

repository: USNM 144362, 144363

### *Palmatolepis quadrantinodosa quadrantinodosa* Branson and Mehl
(Pl. 4, figs. 6, 11)

*Palmatolepis quadrantinodosa* BRANSON AND MEHL, 1934a, Univ. Missouri Studies, v. 8, p. 235–236, Pl. 18, figs. 3, 17, 20

*Palmatolepis (Palmatolepis) sp. aff. crepida* CLARK AND BECKER, 1960, Geol. Soc. America Bull., v. 71, p. 1671, Pl. 2, figs. 4, 5 (not figs. 3, 9, 10)

*Palmatolepis quadrantinodosa quadrantinodosa* ZIEGLER, 1962b, Hess. Landesamt Boden., Abh., no. 38, Pl. 7, figs. 10, 11

remarks: The name species for Ziegler's conodont zone (1962b) in the upper *Cheiloceras* cephalopod zone has been found at only one locality in Nevada. It is not abundant at this locality, but specimens are well preserved.

occurrence: Uppermost *rhomboidea* zone, Devils Gate Formation; sample E-1 of section E, Diamond Range, Nevada (Fig. 4); 5 specimens

repository: BYU 513, 515

### *Palmatolepis quadrantinodosa inflexa* Müller
(Pl. 9, fig. 10)

*Palmatolepis (Palmatolepis) inflexa* MÜLLER, 1956b, Senckenbergischen Naturf. Gesell., Abh., Bd. 494, p. 30–31, Pl. 10, figs. 5a, 5b

*Palmatolepis quadrantinodosa inflexa* ZIEGLER, 1962b, Hess. Landesamt Boden., Ahb., no. 38, p. 73–74, Pl. 7, figs. 1–5

remarks: The Utah specimens appear identical to those described by Müller and by Ziegler.

They are of special importance as they occur in the youngest interval from which conodonts have been reported in the Pilot Shale.

OCCURRENCE: Lower *quadrantinodosa* zone, Pilot Shale; sample collected from the base of unit G-9 of section G, Burbank Hills, western Utah (Fig. 6); 16 specimens

REPOSITORY: USNM 144364

### *Palmatolepis quadrantinodosa marginifera* Ziegler
(Pl. 5, fig. 5)

*Palmatolepis quadrantinodosa marginifera* ZIEGLER, 1960b, Fortschr. Geol. Rheinld. u. Westf., v. 6, p. 11, Pl. 1, fig. 6, Pl. 2, figs. 6–8; ZIEGLER, 1962b, Hess. Landesamt Boden., Ahb., no. 38, p. 75, Pl. 7, figs. 6–9

REMARKS: The marginal folds or ridge which run close and more or less parallel to the carina are distinctive of this species. Müller (1956) included this subspecies and the one described previously in his *P. inflexa*, but Ziegler (1962b) has defined morphologic and stratigraphic differences and the two subspecies can be readily distinguished.

OCCURRENCE: Lower *quadrantinodosa* zone, Pilot Shale; sample collected from base of unit G-9 of section G, Burbank Hills, western Utah (Fig. 6); 6 specimens

REPOSITORY: USNM 145171

### *Palmatolepis rugosa trachytera* Ziegler
(Pl. 7, fig. 12)

*Palmatolepis rugosa trachytera* ZIEGLER *in* KRONBERG, PILGER, SCHERP, AND ZIEGLER, 1960, Fortschr Geol. Rheinld. u. Westf., v. 3, p. 38, Pl. 2, figs. 1–9, Pl. 1, fig. 6, Figs. 12, 13

*Palmatolepis (Palmatolepis) rugosa* BEACH, 1961, Brigham Young Univ. Geol. Studies, v. 8, p. 50, Pl. 5, fig. 16

REMARKS: This species is quite similar to *P. rugosa ampla* but the distinct posterior-directed nodose ridge and the digitate marginal ornamentation suggest a closer relationship to *P. rugosa trachytera*. This is the youngest species of *Palmatolepis* known in the Great Basin.

OCCURRENCE: *Velifera* zone, Pinyon Peak Limestone; samples RS-5, RS-6, RS-12, of Beach's (1961) Rattlesnake Spur section, central Utah (Fig. 8); 8 specimens

REPOSITORY: BYU 1108

### *Palmatolepis subperlobata* Branson and Mehl
(Pl. 8, fig. 16; Pl. 9, figs. 5, 6, 12)

*Palmatolepis subperlobata* BRANSON AND MEHL, 1934a, Univ. Missouri Studies, v. 8, p. 235, Pl. 18, figs. 11, 21; ZIEGLER, 1962b, Hess. Landesamt Boden., Abh., no. 38, p. 79, Pl. 4, figs. 1, 2; GLENISTER AND KLAPPER, 1966, Jour. Paleontology, v. 40, p. 822–823, Pl. 92, figs. 5–7

*Palmatolepis (Palmatolepis) subperlobata* CLARK AND BECKER, 1960, Geol. Soc. America Bull., v. 71, p. 1672, Pl. 2, figs. 14, 16 (not fig. 15)

REMARKS: This species is very similar to *P. triangularis* with which it occurs. European students have used surface ornamentation as a criterion for specific distinction but the two species are transitional.

Two forms figured here (Pl. 9, figs. 6, 12) have larger lobes and are a little different from some identified as *P. subperlobata*. These are from the *rhomboidea* zone.

OCCURRENCE: Middle *Palmatolepis triangularis* zone through lower *crepida* zone and *rhomboidea* zone. Pilot Shale; sample from 4 feet above B-36 of section B; sample 21, 3.5 miles southwest of section C; sample 11, 0.6 mile southwest of section C; and sample C-19 of section C, Confusion Range, western Utah (Figs. 5, 7); *Rhomboidea* zone forms from sample E-1, section E, Diamond Range, Nevada (Fig. 4); more than 100 specimens

REPOSITORY: USNM 144366, 144367, 144368

### *Palmatolepis subrecta* Miller and Youngquist
(Pl. 4, fig. 4; Pl. 9, fig. 9)

*Palmatolepis subrecta* MILLER AND YOUNGQUIST, 1947, Jour. Paleontology, v. 21, p. 513, Pl. 75, figs. 7–11; ZIEGLER, 1962b, Hess. Landesamt Boden., Abh., no. 38, p. 79–80; GLENISTER AND KLAPPER, 1966, Jour. Paleontology, v. 40, p. 823–824, Pl. 88, figs. 1–3

*Palmatolepis (Manticolepis) subrecta* CLARK AND BECKER, 1960, Geol. Soc. America Bull., v. 71, p.
1673, Pl. 1, fig. 12
REMARKS: An individual which is apparently a young form is figured (Pl. 9, fig. 9) along
with the typical *P. subrecta*. Apparently, this species has been commonly misidentified in Europe
and is a long ranging type through several subzones.
OCCURRENCE: Lower and upper *gigas* zones, Pilot Shale; young form from sample 2, 0.5 mile
northeast of section B, and others from sample 12, 0.6 mile southwest of section B, Confusion
Range, western Utah (Fig. 7); more than 100 specimens
REPOSITORY: USNM 144369, BYU 535

*Palmatolepis tenuipunctata* Sannemann
(Pl. 9, fig. 11)

*Palmatolepis tenuipunctata* SANNEMANN, 1955a, Senckenbergiana Lethaea, Bd. 36, p. 136, Pl. 6,
fig. 22, Fig. 2; ZIEGLER, 1962b, Hess. Landesamt Boden., Abh., no. 38, p. 80, Pl. 4, figs.
3–13, Fig. 8; GLENISTER AND KLAPPER, 1966, Jour. Paleontology, v. 40, p. 824, Pl. 89,
fig. 4, Pl. 92, figs. 9–11
REMARKS: This species is similar to both *P. triangularis* and *P. subperlobata* but is more deli-
cately formed and has an unusually sculptured upper surface.
OCCURRENCE: Upper *Palmatolepis triangularis* zone to lower *crepida* zone, Pilot Shale; sample 11,
0.6 mile southwest of section C; sample 3, 0.8 mile northeast of section B; and sample from
unit C-19 of section C, Confusion Range, western Utah (Figs. 5, 7); more than 50 specimens
REPOSITORY: USNM 144370

*Palmatolepis triangularis* Sannemann
(Pl. 9, figs. 7, 13, 14)

*Palmatolepis triangularis* SANNEMANN, 1955b, Neues Jahrbuch Geol. Paläont., Abh., Bd. 100, p.
327, Pl. 24, fig. 3; ZIEGLER, 1962b, Hess. Landesamt Boden., Abh., no. 38, p. 83–85, Pl.
1, figs. 1–16
*Palmatolepis (Palmatolepis) subperlobata* CLARK AND BECKER, 1960, Geol. Soc. America Bull., v. 71,
p. 1672, Pl. 2, fig. 15 (not figs. 14, 16); GLENISTER AND KLAPPER, 1966, Jour. Paleontology,
v. 40, p. 825, Pl. 92, figs. 17, 18
REMARKS: Much of the Great Basin material previously referred to as *P. subperlobata* fits the
definition of *P. triangularis*. The two appear transitional. Surface texture and outline are distinctive
in adult stages.
OCCURRENCE: Middle *Palmatolepis triangularis* zone to lower *crepida* zone; Pilot Shale, Devils
Gate Formation. Sample collected 97 feet above F-5 of section F at Devils Gate Pass, Nevada
(Fig. 3); Pilot Shale samples: 11, 0.6 mile southwest of section C; 21, 3½ miles southwest of
Section C; and sample from unit C-19 of section C, Confusion Range, western Utah (Figs. 5, 7);
more than 100 specimens
REPOSITORY: USNM 144371, 144372, 144373

*Palmatolepis unicornis* Miller and Youngquist
(Pl. 4, fig. 13; Pl. 9, fig. 3)

*Palmatolepis unicornis* MILLER AND YOUNGQUIST, 1947, Jour. Paleontology, v. 21, p. 514, Pl. 75,
fig. 15; GLENISTER AND KLAPPER, 1966, Jour. Paleontology, v. 40, p. 826, Pl. 88, figs. 10, 11
REMARKS: Many specimens of this species are fragmentary and difficult to distinguish from
*P. subrecta*. One figured specimen (Pl. 9, fig. 3) is a young individual of the species. Other speci-
mens and fragments in the collections show clearly the features of this species.
OCCURRENCE: Lower *gigas* zone, Pilot Shale; sample 12 collected from 0.6 mile southwest of
section B, Confusion Range, western Utah (Fig. 7); 15 specimens
REPOSITORY: USNM 144374, BYU 536

*Palmatolepis? ziegleri* n. sp.
(Pl. 7, figs. 1, 2; Pl. 8, figs. 1, 2, 4, 5, 7, 10, 11, 12, 15)

A complete ontogenetic sequence of this species has been found. Younger individuals have
narrow platforms that reach their widest point at about mid-length of carina. On older indi-

viduals the platform maintains a rather constant width throughout. Platform is ornamented with coarse nodes in young- and intermediate-aged individuals but nodes become ridgelike at old age. Outer side of platform is half as wide as inner side. Free blade is only two to three denticles long on younger individuals but six to eight denticles may comprise free blade on older specimens. Carina maintains a constant height and is as high as free blade to a point just anterior of the posterior end where it abruptly decreases to node size. All denticles are fused and crowded for entire length of specimen. Carina slightly curved in younger specimens and straight at maturity.

Aboral surface has prominent keel for the entire length with escutcheon of moderate size located at mid-point of specimen. Crimp prominent.

REMARKS: This species is distinguished by the very short free blade and carina which is as high as the blade for almost the entire length of specimen. The flat platform is narrow and seems to indicate its ancestors were of the *Polygnathellus* group. As suggested under generic description, this form probably originated from *Polygnathellus* by a straightening of the carina. The species is referred to *Palmatolepis* with question as it appears to be so transitional that perhaps it should be assigned to another genus. It is structurally intermediate between *Polygnathellus* and *Palmatolepis* species such as *P. linguiformis*. *Nothognathella sublaevis* Sannemann is different and that species is strongly arched, has a long free blade, and a distinct carina.

Specimens of the species are abundant in the Nevada material and more than 60 individuals of all sizes have been examined for this report.

OCCURRENCE: Middle *dubia* (=*asymmetrica?*) zone, unnamed Upper Devonian formation, Mary's Mountain, Nevada (Fig. 2)

REPOSITORY: USNM 144375 (holotype), 144376, 144377, 144378, 144379, 144380, 144381, 144382

Genus *Pelekysgnathus* Thomas, 1949
Type species: *P. inclinata* Thomas, 1949
*Pelekvsgnathus planus* Sannemann
(Pl. 6, figs. 1, 14)

*Pelekysgnathus planus* SANNEMANN, 1955, Senckenbergiana Lethaea, Bd. 36, p. 149, Pl. 4, fig. 22, 23; BISCHOFF AND ZIEGLER, 1956, Hess. Landesamt Boden., Notizbl., Bd. 84, p. 156, Table 1; ZIEGLER, 1959, Neues Jahrbuch Geol. Paläont., Monatsh., Bd. 7, p. 300; ZIEGLER, 1962b, Hess. Landesamt Boden., Abh., no. 38, p. 52

REDESCRIPTION: Specimens in the Great Basin collections represent immature individuals to gerontic forms. In the early stages of development the denticles of the single series are fused but readily visible through the walls of the semitransparent blade. There are seven to eight erupted teeth but suppressed denticles can be seen between them near their point of origin within the unit. Those denticles anterior to the center of the conodont are inclined anteriorly, whereas those behind the middle lean backward. The front tooth is somewhat larger than those which follow it but is not otherwise differentiated from the rest of the series. Outline of the basal side of the immature forms is rounded at the anterior end and tapers regularly to the sharp posterior extremity. The aboral surface of the unit takes the form of a broad trough with V-shaped transverse section which becomes progressively deeper anteriorly and attains its greatest depth beneath the base of the anterior denticles. In the case of the larger (gerontic) specimens, the basal outline is altered as a result of the marked lateral expansion of the anterior half of the basal excavation. In oral view, the basal flare on one side is semicircular in plan and the corresponding expansion on the opposite side is smaller and subtriangular in shape. The basal cavity beneath the posterior half of such specimens is not significantly wider than the blade. The free ends of the denticles of the larger specimens tend to be developed as short, narrow ribs transverse to the axis of the blade. The tooth above the center of the flared part of the base is unequally developed so that a low ridge extends from its apex down one side of the blade onto the basal expansion.

REMARKS: The conodonts considered here resemble other species of *Pelekysgnathus* in possessing a thin, deep blade which consists of a single series of fused denticles. They are atypical representatives of that genus in that a markedly differentiated cusp is absent although the anterior denticle is somewhat larger than the others. Lack of a distinct cusp and the nearly straight aboral outline are characters suggestive of affinity with *Icriodus*.

OCCURRENCE: Middle *Palmatolepis triangularis* zone through lower *crepida* zone, Pilot Shale. Sample 11, 0.6 mile southwest of section C; sample 21, 3½ miles southwest of section C; and sample from unit C-19 of section C, Confusion Range, western Utah (Figs. 5, 7); 9 specimens

REPOSITORY: USNM 144383, 144384

Genus *Polygnathellus* Bassler, 1925

Type species: *P. typicalis* Bassler, 1925

*Polygnathellus* n. sp.

(Pl. 4, fig. 15; Pl. 5, fig. 8; Pl. 6, fig. 5)

This is a high narrow blade which has denticles basally fused so that they lose their identity but are less fused distally and free at their apices. One tooth, about a third of the way forward, is at least twice the size of the others. Anterior to this position the denticles are long and slender, whereas on the posterior third, they decrease in length toward the extremity so that their sharp points lie along an arc of a circle. On one of the lateral faces, a ridge extends longitudinally at the base of the teeth. At about mid-length it broadens to form a small lateral lobe ornamented on its oral surface with low conical nodes. One or two similar nodes are seated on the ridge near the posterior end. In the corresponding position on the opposite side of the unit, a narrow lobate platform occurs on the posterior two thirds of the unit and narrows anteriorly to form a ridge leading to the anterior extremity. Nodes on the oral surface of the platform are randomly arranged with greatest concentration toward the posterior but with a few fused as far forward as the ridgelike anterior continuation. Aborally, the unit is smooth except for a zone of concentric striae surrounding the longitudinal keel. A subcentral escutcheon continues anteriorly and posteriorly for a short distance as a shallow trough in the edge of the keel.

REMARKS: This form stands close to *Polygnathellus typicalis* Ulrich and Bassler in the development of the apical denticle and teeth of the blade. However, that species does not have the smaller lateral platform or nodes as ornamentation on the one side. Further, the major platform extends the entire length of *P. typicalis*, whereas here it is restricted to about two thirds the length. Greater concentration of the nodes on the platform toward the posterior end suggests possible affinity with *P. similis* Huddle.

One type (Pl. 5, fig. 8) has a sinuous carina and other features which suggest a transition with *Palmatolepis? ziegleri* n. sp. Bischoff and Ziegler (1957, Pl. 21, figs. 4a, 4b, 10, 11) figure a sp. A and a sp. B of *Polygnathellus* which are very similar.

OCCURRENCE: Middle *dubia* (=*asymmetrica?*) zone, unnamed Upper Devonian formation, Mary's Mountain, Nevada (Fig. 2); 15 specimens

REPOSITORY: USNM 144385, 144386, 144387

*Polygnathellus ?* sp.

(Pl. 6, fig. 3)

A single sinuous blade with a noded ridge along the base of the teeth on the convex face characterize this species. All denticles are slightly inclined posteriorly, increase in height at mid-length, and then decrease posteriorly. Outer edge of the oral surface of the platform is set with a row of stout conical nodes. Lower surface is keeled and has a medial escutcheon.

OCCURRENCE: Middle *dubia* (=*asymmetrica?*) zone, unnamed Upper Devonian formation, Mary's Mountain, Nevada (Fig. 2); one specimen

REPOSITORY: USNM 144388

Genus *Polygnathus* Hinde, 1879

Type species: *P. dubia* Hinde, 1879

Hinde (1879) did not designate a type for his concept of *Polygnathus* and this oversight has led to considerable nomenclatural difficulties. Roundy (1926, p. 13) selected the specimen illustrated by Hinde on Plate 16, figure 17 as lectotype of *Polygnathus dubia* and this also became the type for the genus. Unfortunately, the specimen selected is a fragmentary individual and apparently is closer to our present concept of *Ancyrodella* than to *Polygnathus*. *Polygnathus* is widely used and so well-known a name that undue confusion would result if these names were recognized as synonyms. Ziegler and others (1964) recognized this fact and suggested a new type for the genus and at the same time proposed new names for the *P. dubia* group. This problem is still unresolved but pending a satisfactory solution original names are retained for this report.

Recent studies of species of this genus have been published by Müller and Müller (1957), Ziegler (1962a), and Helms (1960). More than 160 species have been proposed and many of these are obvious synonyms. The multiplicity of names has detracted from the biostratigraphic value of the genus.

There appear to be at least three broad morphologic groups now assigned to *Polygnathus*: (1) those with broad flattish platforms ornamented with fine to coarse nodes, *e. g.*, *dubia* (=*asymmetrica?*), *nodocostata*, *ordinata*, *granulosa*, *etc.*; (2) those with free blade and platform of about equal length and with upfolded platform margins, with ornamentation consisting of ribs and/or nodes, *e. g.*, *normalis*, *foliata*, *etc.*; and (3) those with flattish platforms bearing heavy ribs perpendicular to the carina and largely Mississippian, *e. g.*, *longipostica*, *concava*, *symmetrica*, *lanceolata*, *sulcata*, *rugosa*, *etc.*

Most of the described species can probably be accommodated in one of these morphologic groups. A monograph based on such observations could well represent the genus as a more valuable middle Paleozoic "index fossil."

Fifteen species are here described, about half of which are from the *dubia* (=*asymmetrica?*) zone material of western Nevada. In addition, Beach (1961) has described species from the Late Devonian Pinyon Peak and Fitchville formations in central Utah. Brief descriptions of each species are given in order to clarify our interpretation.

### *Polygnathus anomala* Cooper
(Pl. 5, fig. 12)

*Polygnathus anomala* COOPER, 1939, Jour. Paleontology, v. 13, p. 399, Pl. 40, figs. 5, 6; FAY, 1952, Univ. Kansas Paleont. Contrib., Vert., art. 3, p. 150

*P. anomala* is distinguished from other species by its thick asymmetrical platform which bears heavy ridges and nodes and a fused carina. The posterior end is pointed and turned downward and the free blade is heavy. Margins of platform are irregularly warped. The pit is small and located under the junction of the blade and platform.

REMARKS: The figured specimen differs from the type because it has a fused ridge or secondary carina which extends to the margin of the platform.

OCCURRENCE: Middle *dubia* (=*asymmetrica?*) zone, unnamed Upper Devonian formation, Mary's Mountain, Nevada (Fig. 2); 13 specimens

REPOSITORY: USNM 144389

### *Polygnathus brevis* Miller and Youngquist
(Pl. 7, figs. 6, 9)

*Polygnathus brevis* MILLER AND YOUNGQUIST, 1947, Jour. Paleontology, v. 21, p. 514, Pl. 74, fig., 9; FAY, 1952, Univ. Kansas Paleont. Contrib., Vert., art. 3, p. 151

This species is characterized by a short platform and blade, heavy ridges on the platform, and a carina which is distinct for the entire length of the specimen. Ridges are moderately heavy and discontinuous and are most distinct on mature specimens. Platform margins upturned and warped.

OCCURRENCE: Middle *dubia* (=*asymmetrica?*) zone, unnamed Upper Devonian formation, Mary's Mountain, Nevada (Fig. 2); 15 specimens

REPOSITORY: USNM 144390, 144391

### *Polygnathus cristata* Hinde
(Pl. 7, figs. 16, 17)

*Polygnathus cristatus* HINDE, 1879, Geol. Soc. London Quart. Jour., v. 35, p. 366, Pl. 17, fig. 11
*Polygnathus cristata* FAY, 1952, Univ. Kansas Paleont. Contrib., Vert., art. 3, p. 152; BISCHOFF

AND ZIEGLER, 1957, Hess. Landesamt Boden., Abh., no. 22, p. 86–87, Pl. 15, figs. 1a, 1b, 2–12, 13a, 13b, 16, Pl. 17, figs. 12, 13; STOPPEL AND ZIEGLER, 1958, Hess. Landesamt Boden., Notizbl., Bd. 86, p. 157; KREBS, 1959, Senckenbergiana Lethaea, Bd. 40, p. 371, Pl. 1, fig. 16; ZIEGLER, 1962a, Neues Jahrbuch Geol. Paläont., Abh., Bd. 114, p. 151

Strongly arched plate, short free blade. Ornamentation consists of heavy pointed tubercles on the anterior part of the plate which are usually aligned for only a short distance posteriorly. Nodes are less coarse and randomly arranged on posterior two thirds of platform. Deep furrows on either side of carina at anterior end of platform. Escutcheon small and just anterior of center of platform; crimp moderately wide.

REMARKS:  This species is distinct from the similarly ornamented *P. nodocostata* and *P. granulosa* because of the pattern at the anterior part of the platform and the strong arching of the unit. Recently, Ziegler (1962a) has indicated that this species is the morphologic ancestor of the Upper Devonian *Ancyrognathus* group, and Krebs (1959) has shown that the species is one of the good markers for the Middle-Upper Devonian boundary.

OCCURRENCE:  Middle *dubia* ( =*asymmetrica?*) zone, unnamed Upper Devonian formation, Mary's Mountain, Nevada (Fig. 2); 21 specimens

REPOSITORY:  USNM 144392, 144393

### *Polygnathus dengleri* Bischoff and Ziegler
(Pl. 7, figs. 3, 8)

*Polygnathus dengleri* BISCHOFF AND ZIEGLER, 1957, Hess. Landesamt Boden., Abh., no. 22, p. 87–88, Pl. 15, figs. 14, 15, 17–24, Pl. 16, figs. 1–4; STOPPEL AND ZIEGLER, 1958, Hess. Landesamt Boden., Notizbl., Bd. 86, p. 155, 156, 157; ZIEGLER, 1958, Hess. Landesamt Boden., Notizbl., Bd. 87, p. 13, 36, 75; KREBS, 1959, Senckenbergiana Lethaea, Bd. 40, p. 371, 373, 374–376, Pl. 1, figs. 1, 4, 5, 9

Platform slender with irregular nodes and ridges, a short free blade, and a carina which extends to the posterior tip of the platform. Carina is heavy and distinct and on some specimens there is an unornamented area on either side. Specimens slightly arched and posterior end is down-pointed. Platform is usually flat but on larger individuals some warping of margins occurs. Escutcheon is anterior of mid-point of platform, keel prominent, crimp indistinct.

REMARKS:  *P. dengleri* is most closely similar to *P. dubia* ( =*asymmetrica ovalis?*) with which it occurs in Nevada and elsewhere in the world. The ornamentation is more irregular and coarser than that on *P. dubia* ( =*asymmetrica ovalis?*) and only the small individuals of the species are as symmetrical.

OCCURRENCE:  Middle *dubia* ( =*asymmetrica?*) zone, unnamed Upper Devonian formation, Mary's Mountain, Nevada (Fig. 2); 19 specimens

REPOSITORY:  USNM 144394

### *Polygnathus dubia dubia* Hinde ( =*asymmetrica ovalis* Ziegler and Klapper)
(Pl. 7, figs. 14, 15; Pl. 8, figs. 8, 9)

*Polygnathus dubius* HINDE, 1879, Geol. Soc. London Quart. Jour., v. 35, p. 362–365, Pl. 16, figs. 6–18 (in part); FAY, 1952, Univ. Kansas Paleont. Contrib., Vert., art. 3, p. 153

*Polygnathus dubia* BECKMANN, 1949, Senckenbergiana Lethaea, Bd. 30, p. 154–155, Pl. 1, fig. 3, Pl. 2, fig. 10, Pl. 4, fig. 4

*Polygnathus dubia dubia* BISCHOFF AND ZIEGLER, 1957, Hess. Landesamt Boden., Abh., no. 22, p. 88, Pl. 16, figs. 18, 19, Pl. 21, figs. 1, 2; BISCHOFF AND SANNEMANN, 1958, Hess. Landesamt Boden., Notizbl., Bd. 86, p. 102; STOPPEL AND ZIEGLER, 1958, Hess. Landesamt Boden., Notizbl., Bd. 87, p. 155–157; KREBS, 1959, Senckenbergiana Lethaea, Bd. 40, p. 373, 375, 376, 378–380; ZIEGLER, 1962a, Neues Jahrbuch Geol. Paläont., Abh., Bd. 114, p. 146, 147, 151, 156

*Polygnathus asymmetrica ovalis* ZIEGLER, KLAPPER, AND LINDSTRÖM, 1964, Jour. Paleontology, v. 38, p. 422–423; GLENISTER AND KLAPPER, 1966, Jour. Paleontology, v. 40, p. 828, Pl. 87, figs. 8, 9

Flattened, broadly to narrowly symmetrical platform which is arched and bears more or less uniform moderately sized nodes; carina discrete and continuous to posterior tip. Free blade is short, high, and fused to tip. Lower surface has prominent keel; escutcheon is central, crimp indistinct. Platform increases in size in proportion to blade as growth continues.

REMARKS: This species has been considered to be the basic morphologic ancestor of the Polygnathidae. Complete ontogenetic series have been arranged from the Nevada material and the younger specimens are difficult to distinguish from small *P. cristata* and *P. dengleri*. This may be an example of deviation, *e.g.*, the case where the young of different organisms are more similar than are the adults.

Nomenclatural difficulties have been discussed under the genus heading and elsewhere.

OCCURRENCE: Middle *dubia* (=*asymmetrica?*) zone, unnamed Upper Devonian formation, Mary's Mountain, Nevada (Fig. 2); F-24, and F-26, section F, Devils Gate Limestone at Devils Gate Pass, Nevada (Fig. 3); more than 100 specimens

REPOSITORY: USNM 144395, 144396; UW 1008, 1009

*Polygnathus dubia asymmetrica* Bischoff and Ziegler (=*asymmetrica asymmetrica* Bischoff and Ziegler) (Pl. 7, fig. 18)

*Polygnathus dubia asymmetrica* BISCHOFF AND ZIEGLER, 1957, Hess. Landesamt Boden., Abh., no. 22, p. 88–89, Pl. 16, figs. 20–22, Pl. 21, fig. 3; STOPPEL AND ZIEGLER, 1958, Hess. Landesamt Boden., Notizbl., Bd. 86, p. 157; ZIEGLER, 1958, Hess. Landesamt Boden., Notizbl., Bd. 87, p. 13, 14, 35, 37, 75, Pl. 1, figs. 4–6, 8, 10; KREBS, 1959, Senckenbergiana Lethaea, Bd. 40, p. 373, 375, 376, 378–380, Pl. 1, fig. 3; ZIEGLER, 1962a, Neues Jahrbuch Geol. Paläont., Abh., Bd. 114, p. 156

*Polygnathus asymmetrica asymmetrica* ZIEGLER, KLAPPER, AND LINDSTRÖM, 1964, Jour. Paleontology, v. 38, p. 423; GLENISTER AND KLAPPER, 1966, Jour. Paleontology, v. 40, p. 828, Pl. 88, figs. 6, 7

Characteristics as in *P. dubia dubia* (=*asymmetrica ovalis?*) except platform is asymmetrical and one side may become more or less lobelike.

REMARKS: This species differs from its single subspecies only in its asymmetrical platform and it has been considered to be the second stage in the evolution of *Palmatolepis* (Ziegler, 1962a). The extreme members of this species are difficult to separate from *P. transitans*.

OCCURRENCE: Middle *dubia* (=*asymmetrica?*) zone, unnamed Upper Devonian formation, Mary's Mountain, Nevada (Fig. 2); more than 50 specimens

REPOSITORY: USNM 144397

*Polygnathus foliata* Bryant (Pl. 5, fig. 7; Pl. 7, fig. 7)

*Polygnathus foliatus* BRYANT, 1921, Buffalo Soc. Nat. Sci. Bull., v. 13, no. 2, p. 24, Pl. 10, figs. 13–16; FAY, 1952, Univ. Kansas Paleont. Contrib., Vert., art. 3, p. 154

*Polygnathus foliata* HUDDLE, 1934, Bull. Am. Paleontology, v. 21, p. 90, Pl. 8, figs. 14, 15; MÜLLER AND MÜLLER, 1957, Jour. Paleontology, v. 31, p. 1086, Pl. 135, fig. 1; BISCHOFF AND ZIEGLER, 1957, Hess. Landesamt Boden., Abh., no. 22, p. 90, Pl. 4, figs. 1–4; HELMS, 1959, Geologie, v. 8, no. 6, p. 651, Pl. 1, figs. 2, 3, Pl. 4, figs. 3, 4; CLARK AND BECKER, 1960, Geol. Soc. America Bull., v. 71, p. 1671

Long free blade, arched, margins of platform upwarped forming troughs between sides and carina. Ornamentation consists of irregular nodes or ridges usually only poorly developed. Keel present, escutcheon small and on anterior part of platform, crimp broad.

REMARKS: Müller and Müller (1957) have discussed this species in some detail and have indicated that *P. decorosa* of most writers belongs with *P. foliata*. They also indicated that most reports of this species are from the Frasnian.

OCCURRENCE: Middle *dubia* (=*asymmetrica?*) zone, unnamed Upper Devonian formation at Mary's Mountain, Nevada (Fig. 2) and lower *crepida* zone, Pilot Shale, sample C-19 (Figs. 3, 5, 7); 10 specimens

REPOSITORY: USNM 144398, 144403

*Polygnathus independensis* Müller and Müller
(Pl. 5, fig. 14)

*Polygnathus independensis* MÜLLER AND MÜLLER, 1957, Jour. Paleontology, v. 31, p. 1088–89, Pl. 141, figs. 2, 9; KREBS, 1960, Hess. Landesamt Boden., Notizbl., Bd. 88, p. 219

Large, high free blade, narrow platform, arched; ornamentation consists of irregularly arranged discrete rows of medium-sized nodes perpendicular to rim. Carina broad at mid-point of platform, narrows to posterior tip. Keel present, narrow elongate escutcheon on anterior part, crimp broad.

REMARKS: The specimens here assigned to *P. independensis* differ slightly from the type in that the platform is more asymmetrical and the nodes are concentrated toward the posterior part of the broader platform half. On one specimen the narrower side of the platform is almost smooth. Other characteristics appear to be about the same and the Great Basin material may be gerontic.

OCCURRENCE: Middle *Palmatolepis triangularis* and lower *crepida* zones, Pilot Shale; sample 21, 3½ miles southwest of section C; sample C-19, section C, Confusion Range, western Utah (Figs. 5, 7); 4 specimens

REPOSITORY: USNM 144399

*Polygnathus* sp. aff. *P. inornata* Branson

Laterally curved narrow, strongly arched platform with strongly upturned margins; short free blade, distinct carina terminating at posterior end of platform in point. Transverse ridges strongly developed. Pit near anterior end, keel best developed posteriorly, crimp narrow.

OCCURRENCE: The specimens described are very similar to *P. inornata* but are fragmentary and occur in rocks older than those in which this species has been found in Europe. Beach (1961) reported this species in the Lower Mississippian rocks of central Utah. Middle and upper *Palmatolepis triangularis* zones, Pilot Shale; sample 11 from 0.6 mile southwest of section C and sample 21 from 3½ miles southwest of section C, Confusion Range, western Utah (Fig. 7); 3 specimens

REPOSITORY: USNM 144400

*Polygnathus linguiformis* Hinde
(Pl. 7, fig. 10)

*Polygnathus linguiformis* HINDE, 1879, Geol. Soc. London Quart. Jour., v. 35, p. 367, Pl. 7, fig. 15; FAY, 1952, Univ. Kansas Paleont. Contrib., Vert., art. 3, p. 155; BISCHOFF AND ZIEGLER, 1956, Hess. Landesamt Boden., Notizbl., Bd. 84, p. 158–159, Pl. 11, fig. 24; HASS, 1956, U. S. Geol. Survey Prof. Paper 286, p. 17, 18, Pl. 4, figs. 16, 17; ZIEGLER,1956, Hess. Landesamt Boden., Notizbl., Bd. 84, p. 103, Pl. 7, figs. 11, 12, 15–20; STEWART AND SWEET, 1956, Jour. Paleontology, v. 30, p. 270, Pl. 34, figs. 9, 11; RHODES AND DINELEY, 1957, Jour. Paleontology, v. 31, p. 365–366, Pl. 37, figs. 17–19, 21, Pl. 38, fig. 3; TEICHMÜLLER AND ZIEGLER, 1957, Neues Jahrbuch Geol. Paläont., Monatsh., Bd. 6, p. 269, 270; ZIEGLER, 1956, Hess. Landesamt Boden., Notizbl., Bd. 84, p. 103–104, Pl. 7, figs. 11, 12, 15–20; LYS AND SERRE, 1957a, Inst. Français Pétrole, Rev., v. 12, p. 1048, Pl. 5, figs. 5a, 5b; BISCHOFF AND ZIEGLER, 1957, Hess. Landesamt Boden., Abh., no. 22, p. 92–93, Pl. 1, figs. 1–13, Pl. 16, figs. 30–35, Pl. 17, figs. 1–8; BISCHOFF AND SANNEMANN, 1958, Hess. Landesamt Boden., Notizbl., Bd. 86, p. 102; SCHRIEL AND STOPPEL, 1958b, Deutsch. Geol. Gesell. Zeit., Bd. 110, p. 299, 300, 303, 304; STOPPEL AND ZIEGLER, 1958, Hess. Landesamt Boden., Notizbl., Bd. 86, p. 154; ZIEGLER, 1958, Hess. Landesamt Boden., Notizbl., Bd. 87, p. 13, 14, 75; KREBS, 1959, Senckenbergiana Lethaea, Bd. 40, p. 376; ZIEGLER, 1959, Neues Jahrbuch Geol. Paläont., Monatsh., Bd. 7, p. 301; HASS, 1959, U. S. Geol. Survey Prof. Paper 294-J, Pl. 50, fig. 11; CLARK AND BECKER, 1960, Geol. Soc. America Bull., v. 71, p. 1671; ZIEGLER, 1960b, Fortschr. Geol. Rheinld. u. Westf., Bd. 6, p. 3; SPASSOV, 1960, Trav. Géol. Bulgarie, sér Paléont., v. 2, p. 71, Pl. 1, figs. 17, 18; BUDUROV, 1961, Rev. Bulgarian Geol. Soc., v. 22, p. 264, Pl. 1, figs. 5, 8–10, 12; REICHSTEIN, 1962, Geologie, v. 11, Pl. 1, figs. 17, 18; SPASSOV, 1964. Rev. Bulgarian Geol. Soc., v. 25, p. 277, Pl. 1, fig. 4; ORR, 1964, Illinois State Geol. Survey, Circ. 361, p. 16, Pl. 4, figs. 8, 9

This species is characterized by a sharply arched and curved platform which is four to five times as long as the short free blade; posterior one third of the specimen is strongly down-curved and has strong ridges, perpendicular to the carina, becoming dominant on the posterior tip. Broad shallow escutcheon, no keel, broad crimp.

OCCURRENCE: According to Bischoff and Ziegler (1957), this species ranges from the Lower Devonian to the base of the Upper Devonian in Europe. In addition to the Upper Devonian occurrences noted here, the species has been found in a broad zone through the Middle Devonian of the Great Basin (Clark and Ethington, 1966). Middle *dubia* (=*asymmetrica?*) zone, unnamed Upper Devonian formation, Mary's Mountain, Nevada (Fig. 2); 25 specimens

REPOSITORY: USNM 144401

### *Polygnathus normalis* Miller and Youngquist
(Pl. 4, fig. 3; Pl. 5, fig. 10)

*Polygnathus normalis* MILLER AND YOUNGQUIST, 1947, Jour. Paleontology, v. 21, p. 515, Pl. 74, figs. 4, 5; FAY, 1952, Univ. Kansas Paleont. Contrib., Vert., art. 3, p. 156; BISCHOFF, 1956, Hess. Landesamt Boden., Notizbl., Bd. 84, p. 133, Pl. 9, fig. 18; ZIEGLER, 1957, Hess. Landesamt Boden., Notizbl., Bd. 85, p. 72; LYS, SERRE, AND DEROO, 1957, Inst. Français Pétrole, Rev., v. 12, p. 805, Pl. 11, fig. 7, p. 1048–1049, Pl. 6, figs. 1a, 1b; BISCHOFF AND ZIEGLER, 1957, Hess. Landesamt Boden., Abh., no. 22, p. 93–94; MÜLLER AND MÜLLER, 1957, Jour. Paleontology, v. 31, p. 1089, Pl. 135, fig. 9, Pl. 141, fig. 3; STOPPEL, 1958, Hess. Landesamt Boden., Notizbl., Bd. 87, p. 96; STOPPEL AND ZIEGLER, 1958, Hess. Landesamt Boden., Notizbl., Bd. 87, p. 156; ZIEGLER, 1958, Hess. Landesamt Boden., Notizbl., Bd. 87, p. 13, 21, 29, 32, 75; KREBS, 1959, Senckenbergiana Lethaea, Bd. 40, p. 374, 375, 380; HELMS, 1961, Geologie, v. 8, p. 992, Pl. 2, fig. 4; CLARK AND BECKER, 1960, Geol. Soc. America Bull., v. 71, p. 1671; BEACH, 1961, Brigham Young Univ. Geol. Studies, v. 8, p. 49–50, Pl. 6, fig. 6; ETHINGTON AND FURNISH, 1962, Jour. Paleontology, v. 36, p. 1282; ZIEGLER, 1962b, Hess. Landesamt Boden., Abh., no. 38, p. 91; GLENISTER AND KLAPPER, 1966, Jour. Paleontology, v. 40, p. 829–830, Pl. 95, figs. 6, 21, 22

Large high free blade, platform narrow, margins of platform upwarped as high as carina; ornamentation consists of ridges which are perpendicular to carina. Platform arched and gently curved. Escutcheon subcentral, crimp broad, keel prominent.

OCCURRENCE: This is one of the long-ranging species of *Polygnathus* and it is found at the base of the Upper Devonian and in the Lower Mississippian in the Great Basin. Middle *dubia* (=*asymmetrica?*) zone and upper *P. triangularis* zone, Nevada and Utah. Mary's Mountain, Nevada (Fig. 2), and sample 11, Pilot Shale, Confusion Range, Utah (Fig. 7); 23 specimens

REPOSITORY: USNM 144402, 144404

### *Polygnathus ordinata* Bryant
(Pl. 7, figs. 5, 13)

*Polygnathus ordinatus* BRYANT, 1921, Buffalo Soc. Nat. Sci. Bull., v. 13, no. 2, p. 24, Pl. 10, figs. 10, 11; FAY, 1952, Univ. Kansas Paleont. Contrib., Vert., art. 3, p. 158
*Polygnathus ordinata* BISCHOFF AND ZIEGLER, 1957, Hess. Landesamt Boden., Abh., no. 22, p. 94, Pl. 18, figs. 25–31

Flat to slightly arched platform with nodes arranged in rows parallel to carina which remains distinct. Short free blade, ridgelike anterior margins of platform.

REMARKS: This is the "*P. nodocostata*" of the earliest Late Devonian and is very similar to that species from younger intervals. As in the younger species, this form seems to anticipate the *Siphonodella* morphology. Beach (1961) described *P. nodocostata* from the Pinyon Peak Limestone in central Utah associated with *Palmatolepis rugosa trachytera*. No species of this kind is known in the Great Basin between these two occurrences.

OCCURRENCE: Middle *dubia* (=*asymmetrica?*) zone, unnamed Upper Devonian formation, Mary's Mountain, Nevada (Fig. 2); 12 specimens

REPOSITORY: USNM 144405, 144480

*Polygnathus rugosa* Huddle
(Pl. 5, fig. 11)

*Polygnathus rugosa* HUDDLE, 1934, Bull. Am. Paleontology, v. 21, p. 16, 98, 99, Pl. 8, figs. 12, 13;
FAY, 1952, Univ. Kansas Paleont. Contrib., Vert., art. 3, p. 159; BISCHOFF AND ZIEGLER,
1957, Hess. Landesamt Boden., Abh., no. 22, p. 96–97, Pl. 17, figs. 9–11, 15; ZIEGLER,
1958, Hess. Landesamt Boden., Notizbl., Bd. 87, p. 13, 75; KREBS, 1959, Senckenbergiana
Lethaea, Bd. 40, p. 376, 379

Thick, heavy, flat platform with thick transverse ridges extending fanlike from low nodose
carina. Free blade of moderate length. Escutcheon subcentral; carina extends beyond posterior
tip of platform on some specimens to form a pointed tip.

OCCURRENCE: Upper *Palmatolepis triangularis* zone, Pilot Shale; sample 11 from 0.6 mile
southwest of section C, Confusion Range, western Utah (Fig. 7); 5 specimens

REPOSITORY: USNM 144481

*Polygnathus* sp. aff. *P. semicostata* Branson and Mehl

Narrow 'V'-shaped platform, arched with transverse ridges on margin. Short free blade.
Carina prominent on anterior half; ridges are dominant ornamentation on posterior half.

REMARKS: Beach (1961) reported *P. semicostata* from the Pinyon Peak Limestone of central
Utah. Specimens in the present collections are all fragmentary and are similar to *P. linguiformis*
as well as *P. semicostata*.

OCCURRENCE: Lower *gigas* zone, Pilot Shale; sample 12 from 0.6 mile southwest of section
B, Confusion Range, western Utah (Fig. 7); 3 specimens

REPOSITORY: USNM 144493

*Polygnathus webbi* Stauffer
(Pl. 7, fig. 11)

*Polygnathus webbi* STAUFFER, 1938, Jour. Paleontology, v. 12, p. 413, 439, Pl. 53, figs. 25–26,
28–29; FAY, 1952, Univ. Kansas Paleont. Contrib., Vert., art. 3, p. 161; BISCHOFF AND
ZIEGLER, 1957, Hess. Landesamt Boden., Abh., no. 22, p. 100–101, Pl. 5, figs. 7–10

REMARKS: This species is not common in the material studied. It is a strongly arched form
with ridges which extend from the margins toward the nodose carina but which do not reach
the center position. The anterior part of this specimen probably could not easily be distinguished
from the same part of *P. linguiformis*. The posterior tips of the two species are distinct, however.

OCCURRENCE: Middle *dubia* (=*asymmetrica?*) zone, unnamed Upper Devonian formation,
Mary's Mountain, Nevada (Fig. 2); 4 specimens

REPOSITORY: USNM 144482

Genus *Prioniodina* Bassler, 1925
Type species: *P. subcurvata* Bassler, 1925
*Prioniodina alternata* (Bassler)
(Pl. 6, fig. 21)

*Synprioniodina alternata* BASSLER, 1925, Geol. Soc. America Bull., v. 36, p. 219; ULRICH AND
BASSLER, 1926, U. S. National Museum, Proc., v. 68, art. 12, p. 42, Fig. 22; FAY, 1952,
Univ. Kansas Paleont. Contrib., Vert., art. 3, p. 196; SCOTT AND COLLINSON, 1961, Kansas
Geol. Soc., Guidebook, 26th Ann. Field Conf., p. 133, Pl. 2, fig. 7; HASS, 1962, p. 50 *in*
Moore, R. C., *Editor*, Treatise on Invertebrate Paleontology, pt. W.

*Prioniodina alternata* HELMS, 1959, Geologie, v. 8, no. 6, p. 652–653, Pl. 2, fig. 15, Pl. 4, fig. 29;
SPASSOV, 1964, Rev. Bulgarian Geol. Soc., v. 25, p. 277, Pl. 1, fig. 4; SPASSOV, 1965, Trav.
Géol. Bulgarie, sér. Paléont., v. 7, p. 97, Pl. 3, figs. 4, 5

REMARKS: This is one of the many species of *Synprioniodina*, *Prioniodina*, *Euprioniodina*, and
*Neoprioniodus* that have been shown to be linked by transitional specimens. For this reason,
workers studying large collections from strata in which conodonts occur in great numbers have
reported difficulty in separating the material into the existing species (*e.g.*, Sannemann, 1955a;
Helms, 1959). European workers have tended to place some of these genera and species in

synonymy and interpret them as representing long-ranging taxa with broad and, in general, unspecified limits of variation. Most American reports have been conservative and retain the original generic and specific distinctions although recognizing that they are not adequately defined. The problem is further complicated by the fact that earlier students of conodonts adhered to rigid interpretations of type specimens permitting little variation within species. Thus, numerous names have been established, many of which have not been recognized at other than the type locality and some of which are based on inadequate material for study. A careful revision of the entire group is desirable as well as necessary.

OCCURRENCE: Middle *dubia* (=*asymmetrica?*) zone and upper *P. triangularis* zone, Mary's Mountain, Nevada (Fig. 2); sample 11, 0.6 mile southwest of section C, Confusion Range, western Utah (Fig. 7); 3 specimens

REPOSITORY: USNM 144483

Genus *Roundya* Hass, 1953
Type species: *R. barnettana* Hass, 1953

Perhaps this genus should be considered a junior synonym of *Hibbardella*. At present there is no uniform usage of these names but a definite proposal will have to be based on better material than that of the present study.

*Roundya laminata* (Branson and Mehl)
(Pl. 6, fig. 20)

*Trichognathus laminata* BRANSON AND MEHL, 1934a, Univ. Missouri Studies, v. 8, p. 203, Pl. 16, fig. 26
*Trichonodella laminata* FAY, 1952, Univ. Kansas Paleont. Contrib., Vert., art. 3, p. 199

REMARKS: This species is distinguished by the cross section of the apical denticle which is compressed in the anterior-posterior direction with blunt lateral edges. Other species of *Roundya* have a main tooth with circular or laterally compressed cross section.

OCCURRENCE: Upper *Palmatolepis triangularis* zone, Pilot Shale; sample 11, 0.6 mile southwest of section C, Confusion Range, western Utah (Fig. 7); 3 specimens

REPOSITORY: USNM 144484

*Roundya* sp.
(Pl. 6, fig. 22)

Apical denticle oval in cross section, basally erect but curved throughout its length so that it becomes posteriorly inclined toward distal end. Limbs branch laterally and somewhat anterior to position of apical denticle and meet in an angle of 160 degrees in both oral and anterior views. Denticles of limbs are discrete, circular in section, and set deeply into base. Posterior bar broadly convex orally, and sharp aborally. Region beneath apical denticle and near juncture with the limb is flattened although no distinct basal cavity is present.

OCCURRENCE: Lower *crepida* zone, Pilot Shale; sample C-19, section C, Confusion Range, western Utah (Fig. 5); 3 specimens

REPOSITORY: USNM 144485

Genus *Sagittodontus* Rhodes, 1953
Type species: *S. robustus* Rhodes, 1953
*Sagittodontus* sp.
(Pl. 6, fig. 7)

Specimens from the Mary's Mountain locality are robust, deeply excavated distacodontid types. The sharp-pointed cusp has convex faces; it is somewhat recurved at about mid-length. Edges take the form of keels. One lateral margin is straight and the other curved near the base. Basal cavity extends to about two thirds the height of the tooth; anterior and posterior walls are thin. A marked flexure in the basal cavity wall forms a carina-like ridge on the lower half of the outer side, which is shallowly and uniformly convex.

REMARKS: The most common distacodontids reported from the Upper Devonian have been assigned to the genus *Acodina*. They are characteristically slender, compressed, and shallowly excavated. Other simple conical teeth have been assigned to Lower Paleozoic taxa. Occurrence of the distacodontids in Devonian rocks appears sporadic according to their infrequent mention in the many recent reports of conodonts from Europe and North America.

Although the morphology of the Nevada individual necessitates assignment to this genus, no biologic affinity is inferred. It belongs to this morphologic group only. The genus is characteristically developed in Ordovician strata and Müller (1959) reported several species from Upper Cambrian rocks.

OCCURRENCE: Middle *dubia* ( = *asymmetrica?*) zone, unnamed Upper Devonian formation, Mary's Mountain, Nevada (Fig. 2); 3 specimens

REPOSITORY: USNM 144486

Genus *Scutula* Sannemann, 1955

Type species: *S. venusta* Sannemann, 1955

*Scutula venusta* Sannemann

(Pl. 6, fig. 8)

*Scutula venusta* SANNEMANN, 1955a, Senckenbergiana Lethaea, Bd. 36, p. 155, Pl. 4, figs. 6a, 6b, 7; ZIEGLER, 1958, Hess. Landesamt Boden., Notizbl., Bd. 87, p. 21, 29, 32, Pl. 12, figs. 17, 26, 28; STOPPEL, 1958, Hess. Landesamt Boden., Notizbl., Bd. 87, p. 102; HELMS, 1959, Geologie, v. 8, no. 6, p. 657, Pl. 2, figs. 13a, 13b; SERRE AND LYS, 1960, 21st Internat. Geol. Cong., Rept., pt. 6, p. 38; SCHRIEL AND STOPPEL, 1960, Deutsch. Geol. Gesell. Zeit., Bd. 111, p. 670; GLENISTER AND KLAPPER, 1966, Jour. Paleontology, v. 40, p. 835, Pl. 96, fig. 5

REDESCRIPTION: Asymmetrical highly arched blade which is strongly curved along its length. Denticles are slender, erect, and closely crowded although their sharp points are free. Denticles at crest of arch are irregular with one large tooth followed by a number of small ones which are slightly offset toward the concave side of the blade. A denticulated process branches anteriorly from the center of the convex face of the blade and curves sharply downward. The aboral edge of the whole unit is sharp with no evidence for a basal excavation.

REMARKS: One specimen has a narrow vertical flange on one side of the anterior bar and suggests the presence of an incipient lateral branch which is not present on the holotype. The size of the specimen indicates that it is not immature so that this may be a pathologic occurrence. Sannemann reported no particularly well-developed apical denticle in the type material, although his figures suggest that a tooth at the crest of the arched blade is larger and somewhat longer than the others. He further observed that the species is exceedingly variable in character so that the form from western Utah can safely be referred to the species.

OCCURRENCE: *Scutula venusta* has previously been reported in Europe and Australia where it appears in the section toward the top of the *Manticoceras* zone and continues at least through middle Upper Devonian rocks. Middle *Palmatolepis triangularis* zone, Pilot Shale; sample 21, 3½ miles southwest of section C, Confusion Range, western Utah (Fig. 7); 2 specimens

REPOSITORY: USNM 144487

*Scutula sinepennata* Ziegler

(Pl. 6, fig. 16)

*Scutula sinepennata* ZIEGLER, 1958, Hess. Landesamt Boden., Notizbl., Bd. 87, p. 71, Pl. 12, figs. 25, 29; ASH, 1961, Micropaleontology, v. 7, p. 236

Asymmetrical arched and bowed blades with very irregularly developed denticulation. Curvature of the two limbs may be quite unequal and the blade may be either smoothly curved or deflected inward at the top of the arch. Largest denticle is located at the highest point of the unit. Near its base it is parallel to the other teeth but the sharp-edged distal part is usually strongly inclined in the direction of the concave side of the blade. The remaining teeth are relatively uniform in length but vary considerably in width. All have circular cross sections. Unerupted or suppressed denticles can be seen within the blade but are not uniformly distributed along it. The aboral edge is sharp with a very tiny subapical pit.

REMARKS: This species is extremely variable in the curvature of the blade. Some specimens lie nearly in a plane and others are strongly convex. On some specimens the teeth are closely spaced; on others they are separated by open spaces. However, the curved limbs and offset apical denticle serve to identify the species. It is atypical of the other species of *Scutula*, all of which have additional limbs attached at a high angle near the center of the blade.

OCCURRENCE: The species has been reported from the middle *Manticoceras* zone in Germany. Lower *gigas* zone, Pilot Shale; sample 12 from 0.6 mile southwest of section B, Confusion Range, western Utah (Fig. 7); 7 specimens

REPOSITORY: USNM 144488

### *Scutula* sp. aff. *S. bipennata* Sannemann

Sannemann (1955a, p. 154) distinguished *S. bipennata* from *S. venusta* because the former had two lower limbs. Other than this, the two species are quite similar. A single specimen from Utah was broken during studies but it did possess the lower limbs and probably belongs with *S. bipennata*.

This specimen also had some material adhering to the base which resembles the basal attachment material commonly found on species of *Palmatolepis*.

OCCURRENCE: Lower *crepida* zone, Pilot Shale; sample C-19 of section C, Confusion Range, western Utah (Fig. 5); 1 specimen

### Genus *Spathognathodus* Branson and Mehl, 1941
Type species: *Spathodus primus* Branson and Mehl, 1933
### *Spathognathodus gratiosus* (Stauffer)
(Pl. 6, fig. 4)

*Pandorina gratiosa* STAUFFER, 1940, Jour. Paleontology, v. 14, p. 428, Pl. 59, figs. 18–20, 24; FAY, 1952, Univ. Kansas Paleont. Contrib., Vert., art. 3, p. 145
*Pandorina insita* STAUFFER, 1940, Jour. Paleontology, v. 14, p. 429, Pl. 59, figs. 23, 25
*Spathognathodus gratiosus* YOUNGQUIST, 1947, Jour. Paleontology, v. 21, p. 111–112, Pl. 26, fig. 1

REMARKS: Several specimens from the Devonian of the western facies rock appear identical to the type material from Minnesota. Spathognathodids of this type have not been widely reported so that their range is somewhat uncertain. The originally described specimens came from a mixed fauna which included both Ordovician and Upper Devonian conodonts.

OCCURRENCE: Middle *dubia* (=*asymmetrica?*) zone, unnamed Upper Devonian formation, Mary's Mountain, Nevada (Fig. 2); 3 specimens

REPOSITORY: USNM 144489

### *Spathognathodus aculeatus* (Branson and Mehl)
(Pl. 6, fig. 23)

*Spathodus aculeatus* BRANSON AND MEHL, 1934a, Univ. Missouri Studies, v. 8, p. 186–187, Pl. 17, figs. 11, 14
*Spathognathodus aculeatus* ZIEGLER, 1962b, Hess. Landesamt Boden., Abh., no. 38, p. 105–106, Pl. 13, figs. 27–36; GLENISTER AND KLAPPER, 1966, Jour. Paleontology, v. 40, p. 835, Pl. 95, fig. 11 (This reference contains a more complete synonymy.)

REMARKS: This important species has a flaring escutcheon and an offset denticulation above it. Typical representatives of *S. aculeatus* have the anterior denticles of the blade fused together and much longer than the others. This makes the high point of the unit. Our form is likewise high in this area but the denticles seem to be less fused although they are crowded. The posterior ends of the specimens have been lost.

This general type of spathognathodid is known from the Saverton and Louisiana formations of the mid-continent. Collinson and others (1962, p. 18) indicated that the *S. aculeatus* assemblage zone is an easily recognized biostratigraphic unit and that in the Mississippi Valley the species is confined to the middle part of the Saverton and equivalents (*to* V–*to* VI). In Europe, the species is confined to this same interval.

Müller (1962, p. 114) proposed a subgenus *Bispathodus* for all spathognathodids in which more than one series of denticles is present.

OCCURRENCE:   Middle *costatus* zone, Fitchville Formation; sample from unit RS-20 of Rattle-snake Spur section of Beach (1961), central Utah (Fig. 8). This is the youngest Upper Devonian known in the Great Basin area and is the 23rd of Ziegler's (1962b) 24 zones; 3 specimens

REPOSITORY:   USNM 144490

### *Spathognathodus* sp. aff. *S. strigosus* (Branson and Mehl)

REMARKS:   Several specimens appear to have all the characteristics of *S. strigosus* except the presence of swelling on the faces. This may indicate affinity to the several younger species of *Spathognathodus* in which this trend is developed.

OCCURRENCE:   Middle *dubia* (=*asymmetrica?*) zone, unnamed Upper Devonian formation, Mary's Mountain, Nevada (Fig. 2); 3 specimens

REPOSITORY:   USNM 144491

### *Spathognathodus* sp.
### (Pl. 6, fig. 2)

A long thin blade which is somewhat twisted in the posterior half. Aboral edge sharp except for median escutcheon. No prominent basal flare. Denticles fused throughout most of length and nearly equal in size. Unerupted teeth visible between bases of denticle. Oral outline broadly convex. Aboral outline slightly sinuous, somewhat higher posteriorly than anteriorly.

REMARKS:   This is a relatively unspecialized type of the genus which is also close to *S. strigosus*.

OCCURRENCE:   Middle *dubia* (=*asymmetrica?*) zone, unnamed Upper Devonian formation, Mary's Mountain, Nevada (Fig. 2); 10 specimens

REPOSITORY:   USNM 144492

# REFERENCES CITED

ANDERSON, W. I., 1966, Upper Devonian conodonts and the Devonian-Mississippian boundary of north-central Iowa: Jour. Paleontology, v. 40, p. 395–415, Pls. 48–52, 3 figs., 2 tables

ASH, S. R., 1961, Bibliography and index of conodonts 1949–1958: Micropaleontology, v. 7, p. 213–244, 1 fig., 1 table

BASSLER, R. S., 1925, Classification and stratigraphic use of conodonts (Abstract): Geol. Soc. America Bull., v. 36, p. 218–220

BEACH, G. A., 1961, Late Devonian and Early Mississippian biostratigraphy of central Utah: Brigham Young Univ. Geol. Studies, v. 8, p. 37–54, Pls. 5, 6, 5 figs.

BECKMANN, HEINZ, 1949, Conodonten aus dem Iberger Kalk (Ober-Devon) des Bergischen Landes und ihr Feinbau: Senckenbergiana Lethaea, Bd. 30, p. 153–168, 4 pls.

BERGSTRÖM, S. M., AND SWEET, W. C., 1966, Conodonts from the Lexington Limestone (Middle Ordovician) of Kentucky and its lateral equivalents in Ohio and Indiana: Bull. Am. Paleontology, v. 50, no. 229, 441 p., Pls. 28–35, 13 figs., 3 tables.

BISCHOFF, GUNTHER, 1956, Oberdevonische Conodonten (to Iδ) aus dem Rheinischen Schiefergebirge: Hess. Landesamt Boden., Notizbl., Bd. 84, p. 115–137, Pls. 8–10

—— 1957, Die Conodonten-Stratigraphie des rhenoherzynischen Unterkarbons mit Berücksichtigung der *Wocklumeria*-Stufe und der Devon-Karbon-Grenze: Hess. Landesamt Boden., Abh., no. 19, p. 1–64, 6 pls., 1 fig., 2 tables

BISCHOFF, GUNTHER, AND SANNEMANN, DIETRICH, 1958, Unterdevonische Conodonten aus dem Frankenwald: Hess. Landesamt Boden., Notizbl., Bd. 86, p. 87–110, Pls. 12–15

BISCHOFF, GUNTHER, AND ZIEGLER, WILLI, 1956, Das Alter der "Urfer Schichten" im Marburger Hinterland nach Conodonten: Hess. Landesamt Boden., Notizbl., Bd. 84, p. 138–169, Pls. 11–14, 1 table

—— 1957, Die Conodontenchronologie des Mitteldevons und des tiefsten Oberdevons: Hess. Landesamt Boden., Abh., no. 22, p. 1–136, Pls. 1–21, 16 figs., 5 tables

BOND, R. H., 1947, Ohio Shale conodonts: Ohio Jour. Sci., v. 47, p. 21–37, 2 pls.

BOUCKAERT, J., AND ZIEGLER, W., 1965, Conodont stratigraphy of the Famennian Stage (Upper Devonian) in Belgium: Mém. Expl. Cartes Géol. Minieres Belgique, Mem. 5, 62 p., 10 Pls.

BRANSON, E. B., 1944, The geology of Missouri: Univ. Missouri Studies, v. 19, no. 3, p. 1–535, Pls. 1–49

BRANSON, E. B., AND MEHL, M. G., 1934a, Conodonts from the Grassy Creek Shale of Missouri: Univ. Missouri Studies, v. 8, p. 171–259, Pls. 13–21

—— 1934b, Conodonts from the Bushberg Sandstone and equivalent formations of Missouri: Univ. Missouri Studies, v. 8, p. 265–300, Pls. 22–24

—— 1938, The conodont genus *Icriodus* and its stratigraphic distribution: Jour. Paleontology, v. 12, p. 156–166, Pl. 26, 1 fig.

—— 1941, The recognition and interpretation of mixed conodont faunas: Denison Univ. Bull., Sci. Lab. Jour., v. 35, no. 14, p. 195–209

BRANSON, E. R., 1934, Conodonts from the Hannibal formation of Missouri: Univ. Missouri Studies, v. 8, p. 301–343, Pl. 25–28

BRYANT, W. L., 1921, The Genesee conodonts: Buffalo Soc. Nat. Sci. Bull., v. 13, no. 2, p. 1–59, Pls. 1–16, 7 figs.

BUDUROV, K., 1961, Conodonten aus dem Devon Nordostbulgariens: Rev. Bulgarian Geol. Soc., v. 22, p. 259–273, 3 Pls. (in Bulgarian with German summary)

CLARK, D. L., 1954, Stratigraphy and sedimentation of the Gardner formation in central Utah: Brigham Young Univ. Research Studies, Geol. Ser., v. 1, no. 1, 60 p., 4 Pls., 7 tables

CLARK, D. L., AND BEACH, G. A., 1962, Late Devonian-Early Mississippian biostratigraphy, Central Utah, p. 150 *in* The Geological Society of America, Abstracts for 1961: Geol. Soc. America Special Paper 68, 322 p.

CLARK, D. L., AND BECKER, J. H., 1960, Upper Devonian correlations in western Utah and eastern Nevada: Geol. Soc. America Bull., v. 71, p. 1661–1674, 2 Pls., 4 figs., 1 table

CLARK, D. L., AND ETHINGTON, R. L., 1963, Survey of Permian conodonts in western North America: Brigham Young Univ. Geol. Studies, v. 9, pt. 2, p. 102–114, 2 Pls., 1 fig., 1 table
—— 1965, Conodont biostratigraphy of part of the Devonian of the Alberta Rocky Mountains: Canadian Petrol. Geol. Bull., v. 13, p. 382–388, 2 figs.
—— 1966, Conodonts and biostratigraphy of the Lower and Middle Devonian of Nevada and Utah: Jour. Paleontology, v. 40, p. 659–689, Pls. 82–84, 10 figs., 6 tables
CLARK, D. L., SINCAVAGE, J. P., AND STONE, D. D., 1964, New conodont from the Lower Triassic of Nevada: Jour. Paleontology, v. 38, p. 375–377, Pl. 60, 1 fig.
COLLINSON, CHARLES, 1961, The Kinderhookian Series in the Mississippi Valley, p. 100–109 in Kansas Geol. Soc., Guidebook, 26th Ann. Field Conf., 168 p.
COLLINSON, CHARLES, SCOTT, A. J., AND REXROAD, C. B., 1962, Six charts showing biostratigraphic zones, and correlations based on conodonts from the Devonian and Mississippian rocks of the Upper Mississippi Valley: Ill. State Geol. Survey, Circ. 328, p. 1–32, 6 charts
COOPER, C. L., 1931a, Conodonts from the Arkansas novaculite, Woodford formation, Ohio Shale and Sunbury Shale: Jour. Paleontology, v. 5, p. 143–151, Pl. 20
—— 1931b, New conodonts from the Woodford formation of Oklahoma: Jour. Paleontology, v. 5, p. 230–243, Pl. 28
—— 1935, Conodonts from the upper and middle Arkansas novaculite, Mississippian, at Caddo Gap, Arkansas: Jour. Paleontology, v. 9, p. 307–315, Pl. 27
—— 1939, Conodonts from a Bushberg-Hannibal horizon in Oklahoma: Jour. Paleontology, v. 13, p. 379–422, Pls. 39–47, 3 figs.
COOPER, C. L., AND SLOSS, L. L., 1943, Conodont fauna and distribution of a Lower Mississippian black shale in Montana and Alberta: Jour. Paleontology, v. 17, p. 168–176, Pls. 28–29
ELLISON, S. P., JR., AND WYNN, W. T., 1950, Devonian microfossils, Andrews County, Texas: Am. Jour. Sci., v. 248, p. 794–799, 1 Pl., 2 figs.
ETHINGTON, R. L., 1962, Devonian conodonts in Arizona: New Mexico Geol. Soc., Guidebook, 13th Ann. Field Conf., p. 72–76, 1 fig.
—— 1965, Late Devonian and Early Mississippian conodonts from Arizona and New Mexico: Jour. Paleontology, v. 39, p. 566–589, Pls. 67, 68, 1 fig.
ETHINGTON, R. L., AND FURNISH, W. M., JR., 1962, Silurian and Devonian conodonts from Spanish Sahara: Jour. Paleontology, v. 36, p. 1253–1290, Pls. 172–173, 1 fig., 2 tables
ETHINGTON, R. L., FURNISH, W. M., JR., AND WINGERT, J. R., 1961, Upper Devonian conodonts from Bighorn Mountains, Wyoming: Jour. Paleontology, v. 35, p. 759–768, Pl. 90, 1 fig., 1 table
FAY, R. O., 1952, Catalogue of conodonts: Univ. Kansas Paleont. Contrib., Vert., art. 3, p. 1–206, 109 figs.
FLÜGEL, HELMUT, AND ZIEGLER, WILLI, 1957, Die Gliederung des Oberdevons und Unterkarbons am Steinberg Westlich von Graz mit Conodonten: Naturw. Ver. Steiermark, Mitt., Bd. 87, p. 25–60, Pls. 1–5
FREYER, GÜNTER, 1961, Zur Taxionomie und Biostratigraphie der Conodonten aus dem Oberdevon des Vogtlandes unter besonderer Berücksichtigung des to V/VI: Freiberger Forschungs., v. C95, 109 p., 6 Pls., 151 figs.
GLENISTER, B. F., AND KLAPPER, GILBERT, 1966, Upper Devonian conodonts from the Canning Basin, Western Australia: Jour. Paleontology, v. 40, p. 777–842, Pls. 85–96, 3 figs., 9 tables
GRAVES, R. W., JR., 1952, Devonian conodonts from the Caballos novaculite: Jour. Paleontology, v. 26, p. 610–612, Pls. 80–81
GROSS, WALTER, 1960, Über die Basis bei den Gattungen Palmatolepis und Polygnathus (Conodontida): Paläont. Zeit., Bd. 34, p. 40–58
GUTSHICK, R. C., and RODRIGUEZ, JOAQUIN, 1967, Brachiopod zonation and correlation of Sappington Formation of western Montana: Am. Assoc. Petroleum Geologists Bull., v. 51, p. 601–620
HAGUE, ARNOLD, 1892, Geology of the Eureka district, Nevada: U. S. Geol. Survey Mon. 20, 419 p., 7 pls., 9 figs.

HASS, W. H., 1956, Age and correlation of the Chattanooga Shale and the Maury Formation: U. S. Geol. Survey Prof. Paper 286, p. 1–47, Pls. 1–5, 1 fig., 8 tables

—— 1959, Conodonts from the Chappel Limestone of Texas: U. S. Geol. Survey Prof. Paper, 294-J, p. 365–399, Pls. 46–50, 1 fig., 2 tables

—— 1962, Conodonts, p. 3–69 *in* Moore, R. C., *Editor*, Treatise on Invertebrate Paleontology, Part W, Miscellanea: Geol. Soc. America and Univ. Kansas Press, 260 p., 42 figs., 1 table

HELMS, JOCHEN, 1959, Conodonten aus dem Saalfelder Oberdevon (Thuringen): Geologie, v. 8, no. 6, p. 634–677, Pls. 1–6, 3 figs., 2 tables

—— 1960, Die Conodonten-Gattungen *Polvgnathus* und *Palmatolepis* im höheren Oberdevon (Abstract): Paläont. Zeit., Bd. 34, p. 12

—— 1961, Die Bedeutung der Conodonten für die Stratigraphie: Geologie, v. 8, p. 973–995, 3 Pls.

—— 1963, Zur "Phylogenese" und Taxionomie von *Palmatolepis* (Conodontida, Oberdevon): Geologie, no. 12, p. 449–485, 4 Pls., 2 figs.

HIBBARD, R. R., 1927, Conodonts from the Portage Group of western New York: Am. Jour. Sci., 5th ser., v. 13, p. 189–208, Pls. 1–4

HINDE, G . J.,1879, On conodonts from the Chazy and Cincinnati group of the Cambro-Silurian and from the Hamilton and Genesee shale division of the Devonian in Canada and the United States: Geol. Soc. London Quart. Jour., v. 35, pt. 3, p. 351–369, Pls. 15, 17

HINTZE, L. F., 1960a, Preliminary geologic map of the Delta, Utah, 2-degree quadrangle: Brigham Young Univ.

—— 1960b, Preliminary geologic map of the Richfield, Utah, 2-degree quadrangle: Brigham Young Univ.

HOLMES, G. B., 1928, A bibliography of the conodonts with descriptions of early Mississippian species: U. S. National Museum Proc., v. 72, art. 5, p. 1–38, Pls. 1–11

HOSE, R. K., 1966, Devonian stratigraphy of the Confusion Range, west-central Utah: U. S. Geol. Survey Prof. Paper 550-B, p. B36–B41, 2 figs.

HUDDLE, J. W., 1934, Conodonts from the New Albany Shale of Indiana: Bull. Am. Paleontology, v. 21, no. 72, p. 1–136, Pls. 1–12, 3 figs.

KAY, G. MARSHALL, 1947, Analysis of stratigraphy: Am. Assoc. Petroleum Geologists Bull., v. 31, p. 162–168

KLAPPER, GILBERT, 1958, An Upper Devonian conodont fauna from the Darby Formation of the Wind River Mountains, Wyoming: Jour. Paleontology, v. 32, p. 1082–1093, Pls. 141–142, 1 fig., 1 table

—— 1966, Upper Devonian and Lower Mississippian conodont zones in Montana, Wyoming, and South Dakota: Univ. Kansas Paleont. Contrib., Paper 3, 43 p., 6 Pls., 2 figs., 1 table

KLAPPER, GILBERT, AND FURNISH, W. M., 1963, Conodont zonation of the early Upper Devonian in eastern Iowa: Iowa Acad. Sci., Proc. 1962, v. 69, p. 400–410, 2 figs.

KREBS, WOLFGANG, 1959, Zur Grenze Mittel-/Ober-Devon und zur Gliederung des obersten Mittel-Devons und der tieferen Adorf-Stufe nach Conodonten: Senckenbergiana Lethaea, Bd. 40, p. 367–387, Pl. 1, 1 fig.

—— 1960, Neue Ergebnisse zur Stratigraphie des Oberdevons und Unterkarbons in der süd-westlichen Dill-Mulde (Rheinisches Schiefergebirge): Hess. Landesamt Boden., Notizbl., Bd. 88, p. 216–242

KRONBERG, PETER, PILGER, ANDREAS, SCHERP, ADALBERT, AND ZIEGLER, WILLI, 1960, I. Zu den altvariscischen Bewegungen an der Wende Devon/Karkon: Fortschr. Geol. Rheinld. u. Westf., v. 3, p. 1–46, 7 Pls., 13 figs., 3 tables

LANGENHEIM, R. L., JR., 1960, The Pilot Shale, the West Range Limestone, and the Devonian-Mississippian boundary in eastern Nevada: Ill. State Acad. Sci. Trans., v. 53, p. 122–131, 3 figs.

LINDGREN, W., AND LOUGHLIN, G. F., 1919, Geology and ore deposits of the Tintic mining district: U. S. Geol. Survey Prof. Paper 107, 282 p., 39 Pls., 49 figs.

LINDSTRÖM, MAURITS, 1964, Conodonts: Amsterdam, Elsevier Publishing Co., 196 p., 64 figs.

Lys, Maurice, and Serre, Bernedette, 1957a, Étude de conodontes du dévonien et du carbonifère de la région d'Adrar-Tanezrouft (Sahara): Inst. Français Pétrole, Rev., v. 12, p. 1035–1066, Pls. 1–7, 1 fig., 1 table

—— 1957b, Présence de conodontes dans le paléozoïque du Sahara (région d'Adrar-Tanezrouft): Paris, Acad. Sci. Comptes Rendus, v. 244, p. 916–918

Lys, Maurice, Serre, Bernedette, and Deroo, G., 1957, Études micropaléontologiques dans le paléozoïque de la Montagne Noire: Inst. Français Pétrole., Rev., v. 12, p. 783–809, Pls. 1–13, 3 figs., 1 table

Merriam, C. W., 1940, Devonian stratigraphy and paleontology of the Roberts Mountains region, Nevada: Geol. Soc. America Special Paper 25, 114 p., 16 Pls., 7 figs., 8 tables

—— 1963, Paleozoic rocks of Antelope Valley, Eureka and Nye counties, Nevada: U. S. Geol. Survey Prof. Paper 423, 67 p., 2 Pls., 8 figs., 2 tables

Miller, A. K., and Youngquist, Walter, 1947, Conodonts from the type section of the Sweetland Creek Shale, Iowa: Jour. Paleontology, v. 21, p. 501–517, Pls. 72–75

Morris, H. T., 1957, General geology of the East Tintic Mountains, Utah, p. 1–56 in Geology of the East Tintic Mountains and ore deposits of the Tintic mining districts: Utah Geol. Soc. Guidebook 12, 145 p.

Morris, H. T., and Lovering, T. S., 1961, Stratigraphy of the East Tintic Mountains, Utah: U. S. Geol. Survey Prof. Paper 361, 145 p., 5 Pls., 61 figs., 18 tables

Mosher, L. C., and Clark, D. L., 1965, Middle Triassic conodonts from the Prida Formation of northwestern Nevada: Jour. Paleontology, v. 39, p. 551–565, Pls. 65, 66, 2 figs., 1 table

Müller, J. K., 1956a, Taxonomy, nomenclature, orientation, and stratigraphic evaluation of conodonts: Jour. Paleontology, v. 30, p. 1324–1340, Pl. 145

—— 1956b, Die Gattung Palmatolepis: Senckenbergischen Naturf. Gesell., Abh., Bd. 494, p. 1–70, Pls. 1–11, 2 tables

—— 1959, Kambrische Conodonten: Deutsch. Geol. Gesell. Zeit., Bd. 111, p. 434–465, Pls. 11–15, 11 figs., 3 tables

—— 1962, Zur systematischen Einteilung der Conodontophorida: Paläont. Zeit., Bd. 36, p. 109–117, 1 fig.

Müller, J. K., and Clark, D. L., in press, Early Late Devonian conodonts from the Squaw Bay formation in Michigan: Jour. Paleontology

Müller, J. K., and Müller, E. M., 1957, Early Upper Devonian (Independence) conodonts from Iowa, Part I: Jour. Paleontology, v. 31, p. 1069–1108, Pls. 135–142, 8 figs., 2 tables

Nolan, T. B., 1935, The Gold Hill Mining District, Utah: U. S. Geol. Survey Prof. Paper 177, 172 p.

Nolan, T. B., Merriam, C. W., and Williams, J. S., 1956, The stratigraphic section in the vicinity of Eureka, Nevada: U. S. Geol. Survey Prof. Paper 276, 77 p., 2 Pls., 2 figs.

Orr, R. W., 1964, Conodonts from the Devonian Lingle and Alto formations of southern Illinois: Illinois State Geol. Survey, Circ. 361, 28 p., 4 Pls., 4 figs., 2 tables

Panseri, C., and Barsotti, G., 1959, Conodontos y Ostracodos devonianos de la region de Semara (Sahara espanol): Extracto del Inst. Geol. minero España Notas y comun., no. 55, p. 145–176, Pls. 1–4

Reichstein, Manfred, 1962, Die Stratigraphie der Hercynkalke bei Güntersberge im Unterharz und das Problem der Hercynkalkentstehung: Geologie, v. 11, 73 p., 1 Pl., 31 figs.

Rhodes, F. H. T., and Dineley, D. L., 1957, Devonian conodont faunas from southwest England: Jour. Paleontology, v. 31, p. 353–369, Pls. 37–38, 10 figs., 1 table

Rigby, J. K., and Clark, D. L., 1962, Devonian and Mississippian systems in Central Utah: Brigham Young Univ. Geol. Studies, v. 9, pt. 1, p. 17–25, 3 figs.

Roberts, R. J., Hotz, P. E., Gilluly, James, and Ferguson, H. G., 1958, Paleozoic rocks of north-central Nevada: Am. Assoc. Petroleum Geologists Bull., v. 42, p. 2813–2857, 11 figs.

Roundy, P. V., 1926, The micro-fauna, p. 5–23, Pls. 1–4 in Roundy, P. V., Girty, G. H., and Goldman, M. I., Mississippian formations in San Saba County, Texas: U. S. Geol. Survey Prof. Paper 146, 63 p., 33 Pls.

Sannemann, Dietrich, 1955a, Oberdevonische Conodonten (to II α): Senckenbergiana Lethaea, Bd. 36, p. 123–156, 6 Pls., 1 fig.

—— 1955b, Beitrag zur Untergliederung des Oberdevons nach Conodonten: Neues Jahrbuch Geol. Paläont., Abh., Bd. 100, p. 324–331, Pl. 24

Schriel, Walter, 1958, Das Alter des sogenannten Hauptquarzits im südlichen Unterharz und in der Selkemulde: Deutsch. Geol. Gesell. Zeit., Bd. 110, p. 293–306

Schriel, Walter, and Stoppel, Dieter, 1958a, Das Alter der Hauptkieselschiefer Lossen's und der Bunterschiefer in der Südharzmulde: Deutsch. Geol. Gesell. Zeit., Bd. 109, p. 559–565

—— 1958b, Acker-Bruchberg und Kellerwald—Stratigraphie und Tektonik: Deutsch. Geol. Gesell. Zeit., Bd. 110, p. 260–292, 5 figs., 3 tables

—— 1960, Die Einstufung des Tanner Grauwackensystems im Harz auf Grund von Conodonten: Deutsch. Geol. Gesell. Zeit., Bd. 111, p. 662–683, 4 figs.

Scott, A. J., and Collinson, C. W., 1961, Conodont faunas from the Louisiana and McCraney formations of Illinois, Iowa, and Missouri, p. 110–142, 5 figs. in Kansas Geol. Soc., Guidebook, 26th Ann. Field Conf., 168 p.

Serre, Bernedette, and Lys, Maurice, 1960, Repartition de quelques conodontes dans le Dévonien et le Carbonifère inférieur de France et de Belgique: 21st Internat. Geol. Cong., Copenhagen, 1960, Rept., pt. 6, p. 35–40, 3 figs.

Spassov, Hristo, 1960, Paläozoische Conodontenfauna aus südwest-Bulgarien und Ostserbien: Trav. Géol. Bulgarie, sér. Paléont., v. 2, p. 63–75, 1 Pl., 1 fig. (in Bulgarian with German summary)

—— 1964, Beitrag zur Stratigraphie des Silurs und Devons im Kraište: Rev. Bulgarian Geol. Soc., v. 25, p. 267–283, 2 Pls., 1 fig.

—— 1965, Das Karbonatische Oberdevon im Kraište und seine Conodontenfauna: Trav. Geol. Bulgarie, sér. Paléont., v. 7, p. 71–113, 3 Pls., Figs. 1–4, A–L (in Bulgarian with German summary)

Spassov, Hristo, and Stevanović, Petar, 1962, Oberdevonische Conodonten aus Družetić im Westlichen Serbien: Annales Géol. Péninsule Balkanique, v. 29, p. 54–65, 2 Pls. (in Bulgarian with German summary)

Spencer, A. C., 1917, The geology and ore deposits of Ely, Nevada: U. S. Geol. Survey Prof. Paper 96, 189 p., 15 pls., 3 figs.

Stauffer, C. R., 1938, Conodonts of the Olentangy Shale: Jour. Paleontology, v. 12, p. 411–443, Pls. 48–53

—— 1940, Conodonts from the Devonian and associated clays of Minnesota: Jour. Paleontology, v. 14, p. 417–435, Pls. 58–60

Stauffer, C. R., and Plummer, H. J., 1932, Texas Pennsylvanian conodonts and their stratigraphic relations: Univ. Texas Bull., no. 3201, p. 13–50, Pls. 1–4

Stewart, G. A., and Sweet, W. C., 1956, Conodonts from the Middle Devonian Bone Beds of central and west-central Ohio: Jour. Paleontology, v. 30, p. 261–273, Pls. 33, 34, 1 fig., 1 table

Stoppel, Dieter, 1958, Das Oberdevon und Unterkarbon im südlichen Kellerwald: Hess. Landesamt Boden., Notizbl., Bd. 87, p. 89–119

Stoppel, Dieter, and Ziegler, Willi, 1958, Zum Alter der "Buchenauer Schichten" bei Buchenau/Lahn (Rheinisches Schiefergebirge): Hess. Landesamt Boden., Notizbl., Bd. 86, p. 153–158, 1 fig.

Teichmüller, Rolf, and Ziegler, Willi, 1957, Devonkalk-Gerolle im Zechsteinkonglomerate von Rossenray (südwestlich Rheinberg/Niederrhein): Neues Jahrbuch Geol. Paläont., Monatsh., Bd. 6, p. 267–274, 1 fig.

Ulrich, E. O., and Bassler, R. S., 1926, A classification of the toothlike fossils, conodonts, with descriptions of American Devonian and Mississippian species: U. S. National Museum, Proc., v. 68, art. 12, p. 1–63, Pls. 1–11, 5 figs.

Youngquist, W. L., 1945, Upper Devonian conodonts from the Independence Shale (?) of Iowa: Jour. Paleontology, v. 19, p. 355–367, Pls. 54–56

YOUNGQUIST, W. L., 1947, A new Upper Devonian conodont fauna from Iowa: Jour. Paleontology, v. 21, p. 95–112, Pls. 24–26

YOUNGQUIST, W. L., AND DOWNS, R. H., 1951, Conodonts from the Lower Mississippian Wassonville Dolomite of Iowa: Jour. Paleontology, v. 25, p. 785–792, Pl. 111

YOUNGQUIST, W. L., AND MILLER, A. K., 1948, Additional conodonts from the Sweetland Creek Shale of Iowa: Jour. Paleontology, v. 22, p. 440–450, Pls. 67, 68

YOUNGQUIST, W. L., AND PETERSON, R. F., 1947, Conodonts from the Sheffield Formation of north-central Iowa: Jour. Paleontology, v. 21, p. 242–253, Pls. 36–38

ZIEGLER, WILLI, 1956, Unterdevonische Conodonten, insbesondere aus dem Schönauer und dem Zorgensis-Kalk: Hess. Landesamt Boden., Notizbl., Bd. 84, p. 93–106, Pls. 6, 7, 1 table

—— 1957, Das Marburger Gotlandium: Hess. Landesamt Boden., Notizbl., Bd. 85, p. 67–74, 4 figs.

—— 1958, Conodontenfeinstratigraphische Untersuchungen an der Grenze Mitteldevon/Oberdevon und in der Adorfstufe: Hess. Landesamt Boden., Notizbl., Bd. 87, p. 7–77, Pls. 1–12, 7 figs., 10 tables

—— 1959, Conodonten aus Devon und Karbon Südwesteuropas und Bemerkungen zur bretonischen Faltung: Neues Jahrbuch Geol. Paläont. Monatsh., Bd. 7, p. 289–309, 3 figs., 1 table

—— 1960a, Conodonten aus dem Rheinischen Unterdevon (Gedinnium) des Remscheider Sattels (Rheinisches Schiefergebirge): Paläont. Zeit., Bd. 34, p. 169–201, Pls. 13–15, 2 figs., 3 tables

—— 1960b, Die Conodonten aus den Geröllen des Zechsteinkonglomerates von Rossenray (südwestlich Rheinberg/Niederrhein): Fortschr. Geol. Rheinld. u. Westf., v. 6, p. 1–15, 4 Pls., 1 fig.

—— 1962a, Phylogenetische Entwicklung stratigraphisch wichtiger Conodonten-Gattungen in der Manticoceras-Stufe (Oberdevon, Deutschland): Neues Jahrbuch Geol. Paläont., Abh., Bd. 114, p. 142–168, 9 figs.

—— 1962b, Taxionomie und Phylogenie Oberdevonischer Conodonten und ihre stratigraphische Bedeutung: Hess. Landesamt Boden., Abh., no. 38, p. 1–166, 14 Pls., 18 figs., 11 tables

ZIEGLER, WILLI, KLAPPER, GILBERT, AND LINDSTRÖM, MAURITS, 1964, The validity of the name Polygnathus (Conodonta, Devonian and Lower Carboniferous): Jour. Paleontology, v. 38, p. 421–423

E<small>XPLANATION</small> <small>OF</small> P<small>LATES</small> 1-9

PLATE 1.   Possible *Palmatolepis* assemblage
(All figures × 42)

Growth sequence in dextral and sinistral specimens of *Palmatolepis delicatula* is shown in one possible assemblage. Inner side of larger specimen forms good fit with outer side of next smaller size. Arrangement with carina and blade facing inward on all elements of pairs is in accord with orientation of known natural assemblages and with the Lindström theory of lophophore structure. Nutrient-carrying currents passing such an arrangement would be forced toward center of assemblage and perhaps some mouthlike structure.

All specimens from sample 11, upper *P. triangularis* zone, UW 1002.

PLATE 2.   Species of *Acodina*, *Ancyrodella*, *Ancyrognathus*, *Angulodus*,
*Apatognathus*, *Bryantodus*, and *Enantiognathus*
(All figures × 42 except 15, which is × 34)

Figures

1. *Apatognathus varians* Branson and Mehl, *Ancyrognathus triangularis* zone, sample 2, Guilmette Formation, Confusion Range, Utah (Fig. 5), UW 1001

2. *Enantiognathus lipperti* (Bischoff), lower *gigas* zone, sample 12, Pilot Shale, Confusion Range, Utah (Fig. 7), USNM 144318

3. *Acodina curvata* Stauffer, middle *P. triangularis* zone, sample 21, Pilot Shale, Confusion Range, Utah (Fig. 7), USNM 144306

4, 6–10, 13–15. *Ancyrodella rotundiloba* (Bryant), middle *dubia* ( =*asymmetrica?*) zone, Mary's Mountain, Nevada, figures representing growth stages, basal views (6, 13), and random node distribution (9, 14, 15) as well as "cross" pattern (4, 7, 8, 10), 4, USNM 144311; 6, USNM 144315; 7, USNM 144309; 8, USNM 144310; 9, upper, and 13, lower, USNM 144313; 10, USNM 144308; 14, USNM 144314; 15, USNM 144312

5. *Ancyrognathus triangularis* Youngquist, lower *gigas* zone, sample 12, Pilot Shale, Confusion Range, Utah (Fig. 7), USNM 144316

11. *Bryantodus germanus* Ulrich and Bassler, middle *dubia* ( =*asymmetrica?*) zone, Mary's Mountain, Nevada (Fig. 2), USNM 144319

12. *Angulodus demissus* Huddle, middle *dubia* ( =*asymmetrica?*) zone, Mary's Mountain, Nevada (Fig. 2), USNM 144317

PLATE 3.   Species of *Bryantodus, Ctenopolygnathus, Diplododella, Hindeodella, Icriodus, Ligonodina,* and *Lonchodina*
(All figures × 42)

Figures

1, 2.  *Icriodus expansus* Branson and Mehl, middle *dubia* (=*asymmetrica?*) zone, Mary's Mountain, Nevada (Fig. 2), lower and upper views, USNM 144332, 144333

3, 4.  *Icriodus cornutus* Sannemann, middle *P. triangularis* zone, upper and lower views, figured specimen from sample F-6, Devils Gate Formation, Devils Gate Pass, Nevada (Fig. 3), USNM 144328, 144329

5.  *Ligonodina acuta* Branson and Mehl, upper *P. triangularis* zone, sample 11, Pilot Shale, Confusion Range, Utah (Fig. 7), USNM 144336

6.  *Ligonodina delicata* Branson and Mehl, middle *dubia* (=*asymmetrica?*) through upper *P. triangularis* zones, specimen figured from *dubia* (=*asymmetrica?*) zone, Mary's Mountain, Nevada (Fig. 2), USNM 144337

7.  *Diplododella alternata* Branson and Mehl, middle *dubia* (=*asymmetrica?*) zone, Mary's Mountain, Nevada (Fig. 2), USNM 144325

8.  *?Bryantodus grahami* Stauffer, lower *gigas* zone, sample 12, Pilot Shale, Confusion Range, Utah (Fig. 7), USNM 144320

9.  *Ctenopolygnathus omala* (Cooper), middle *dubia* (=*asymmetrica?*) zone, Mary's Mountain, Nevada (Fig. 2), USNM 144324

10.  *Bryantodus masculus* Youngquist and Miller, middle *dubia* (=*asymmetrica?*) zone, Mary's Mountain, Nevada (Fig. 2), USNM 144321

11.  *Icriodus parvus* Youngquist and Peterson, middle *P. triangularis* zone, sample 21, Pilot Shale, Confusion Range, Utah (Fig. 7), USNM 144334

12.  *Lonchodina acutula* Huddle, middle *dubia* (=*asymmetrica?*) zone, Mary's Mountain, Nevada (Fig. 2), USNM 144338

13.  *Icriodus curvatus* Branson and Mehl, *rhomboidea* zone, sample E-1, Devils Gate Formation, Diamond Mountains, Nevada (Fig. 4), USNM 144330

14.  *Bryantodus multidens* Ulrich and Bassler, upper *P. triangularis* zone, sample 11, Pilot Shale, Confusion Range, Utah (Fig. 7), USNM 144322

15.  *Hindeodella subtilis* Bassler, *A. triangularis* through *crepida* zones, figured specimen from sample 11, Pilot Shale, Confusion Range, Utah (Fig. 7), USNM 144327

16.  *Icriodus rectus* Youngquist and Peterson, upper *P. triangularis* zone, sample 11, Pilot Shale, Confusion Range, Utah (Fig. 7), USNM 144335

17.  *Ctenopolygnathus iowaensis* (Youngquist and Peterson), middle *P. triangularis* zone, sample F-5, Devils Gate Limestone, Devils Gate Pass, Nevada (Fig. 3), USNM 144323

18.  *Hindeodella minuta* Branson and Mehl, middle *P. triangularis* zone, sample 21, Pilot Shale, Confusion Range, Utah (Fig. 7), USNM 144326

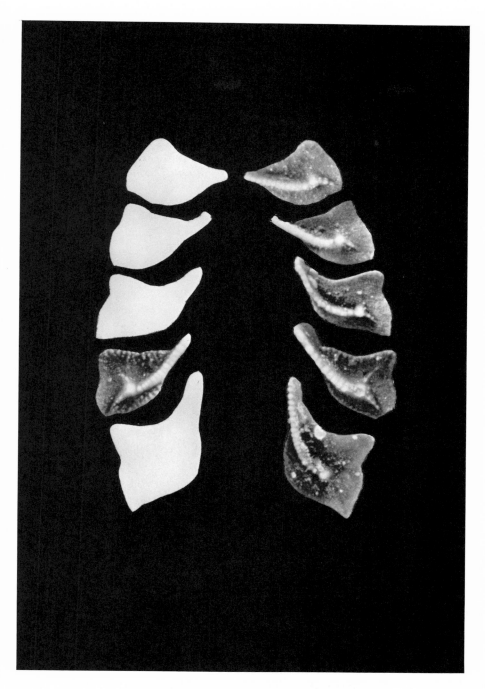

Possible *Palmatolepis* assemblage

Species of *Acodina*, *Ancyrodella*, *Ancyrognathus*, *Angulodus*, *Apatognathus*, *Bryantodus*, and *Enantiognathus*

PLATE 4.   Species of *Hindeodella*, *Ozarkodina*, *Palmatolepis*, *Polygnathellus*,
and *Polygnathus*
(All figures × 30 except 1, 9, 10, 12, 14, which are × 42)

Figures

1. *Hindeodella unca* Bischoff, middle *dubia* ( =*asymmetrica?*) zone, Mary's Mountain, Nevada (Fig. 2), USNM 144341

2. *Ozarkodina macra* Branson and Mehl, lower *crepida* zone, sample C-19, Pilot Shale, Confusion Range, Utah (Fig. 5), USNM 144356

3. *Polygnathus normalis* Miller and Youngquist, middle *dubia* ( =*asymmetrica?*) zone, Mary's Mountain, Nevada (Fig. 2), USNM 144402

4. *Palmatolepis subrecta* Miller and Youngquist, *gigas* zone, sample 12, Pilot Shale, Confusion Range, Utah (Fig. 7), BYU 535

5. *Palmatolepis perlobata schindewolfi* Müller, *quadrantinodosa* zone?, sample 22, Pilot Shale, Confusion Range, Utah (Fig. 7), BYU 522

6, 11. *Palmatolepis quadrantinodosa quadrantinodosa* Branson and Mehl, *rhomboidea* zone, sample E-1, Devils Gate Formation, Diamond Mountains, Nevada (Fig. 4), BYU 513, 515

7, 10. *Palmatolepis coronata* Müller, lower *crepida* zone, sample C-19, Pilot Shale, Confusion Range, Utah (Fig. 5), BYU 527, USNM 144358

8. *Palmatolepis glabra pectinata* Ziegler, *rhomboidea* zone, sample E-1, Devils Gate Formation, Diamond Mountains, Nevada (Fig. 4), BYU 517

9, 14. *Palmatolepis delicatula clarki* Ziegler, middle and upper *P. triangularis* zones, figured specimens from sample 21, Pilot Shale, Confusion Range, Utah (Fig. 7), USNM 114359, 114360

12. *Palmatolepis delicatula delicatula* Branson and Mehl, middle and upper *P. triangularis* zones, figured specimen from sample 21, Pilot Shale, Confusion Range, Utah (Fig. 7), USNM 144361

13. *Palmatolepis unicornis* Miller and Youngquist, *A. triangularis* and lower *gigas* zones, sample 12, Pilot Shale, Confusion Range, Utah (Fig. 7), BYU 536

15. *Polygnathellus* n. sp., middle *dubia* ( =*asymmetrica?*) zone, Mary's Mountain, Nevada (Fig. 2), USNM 144386

16. *Palmatolepis linguiformis* Müller, upper *gigas* zone, sample 2, Pilot Shale, Confusion Range, Utah (Fig. 7), BYU 538

17. *Palmatolepis crepida* Sannemann, *rhomboidea* zone, sample E-1, Devils Gate Formation, Diamond Mountains, Nevada (Fig. 4), BYU 516

18. *Palmatolepis glabra* n. subspecies A Ziegler, *rhomboidea* zone, sample E-1, Devils Gate Formation, Diamond Mountains, Nevada (Fig. 4), BYU 523

19. *Palmatolepis gigas* Miller and Youngquist, *A. triangularis* through upper *gigas* zones, figured specimen from sample 12, Pilot Shale, Confusion Range, Utah (Fig. 7), USNM 144365

PLATE 5.   Species of *Lonchodina, Nothognathella, Ozarkodina, Palmatolepis,*
*Polygnathellus,* and *Polygnathus*
(All figures × 42 except 5 and 7, which are × 30)

Figures

1. *Nothognathella reversa* Branson and Mehl, upper *P. triangularis* zone, sample 11, Pilot Shale, Confusion Range, Utah (Fig. 7), UW 1003

2. *Ozarkodina macra* Branson and Mehl, middle *P. triangularis* zone, sample 21, Pilot Shale, Confusion Range, Utah (Fig. 7), UW 1004

3. *Lonchodina* sp., specimen showing basal attachment material, middle *P. triangularis* zone, sample 21, Pilot Shale, Confusion Range, Utah (Fig. 7), USNM 144344

4. *Lonchodina robusta* Branson and Mehl, lower and upper *gigas* zones, figured specimen from sample 12, Pilot Shale, Confusion Range, Utah (Fig. 7), USNM 144340

5. *Palmatolepis quadrantinodosa marginifera* Ziegler, lower *quadrantinodosa* zone, sample G-9, Pilot Shale, Burbank Hills, Utah (Fig. 6), USNM 145171

6. *Lonchodina arcuata* Ulrich and Bassler, middle *dubia* (=*asymmetrica?*) zone, Mary's Mountain, Nevada (Fig. 2), USNM 144339

7. *Polygnathus foliata* Bryant, middle *dubia* (=*asymmetrica?*) zone, Mary's Mountain, Nevada (Fig. 2), USNM 144403

8. *Polygnathellus* n. sp., middle *dubia* (=*asymmetrica?*) zone, Mary's Mountain, Nevada (Fig. 2), USNM 144387

9. *Lonchodina* sp. aff. *L. arcuata* Ulrich and Bassler, upper *P. triangularis* zone, sample 11, Pilot Shale, Confusion Range, Utah (Fig. 7), USNM 144343

10. *Polygnathus normalis* Miller and Youngquist, upper *P. triangularis* zone, sample 11, Pilot Shale, Confusion Range, Utah (Fig. 7), USNM 144404

11. *Polygnathus rugosa* Huddle, upper *P. triangularis* zone, sample 11, Pilot Shale, Confusion Range, Utah (Fig. 7), USNM 144481

12. *Polygnathus anomala* Cooper, middle *dubia* (=*asymmetrica?*) zone, Mary's Mountain, Nevada (Fig. 2), USNM 144389

13. *Lonchodina typicalis* Bassler, middle *P. triangularis* zone, sample 97 feet above F-5, Devils Gate Formation, Devils Gate Pass, Nevada (Fig. 3), USNM 144342

14. *Polygnathus independensis* Müller and Müller, middle *P. triangularis* and lower *crepida* zones, figured specimen from sample 21, Pilot Shale, Confusion Range, Utah (Fig. 7), USNM 144399

Species of *Bryantodus*, *Ctenopolygnathus*, *Diplododella*, *Hindeodella*, *Icriodus*, *Ligonodina*, and *Lonchodina*

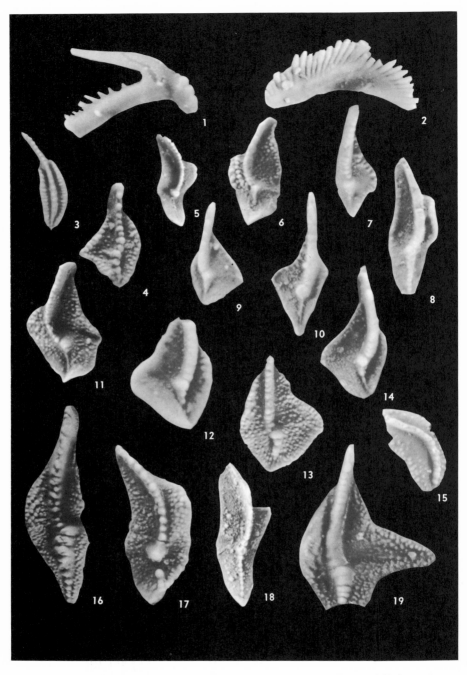

Species of *Hindeodella*, *Ozarkodina*, *Palmatolepis*, *Polygnathellus*, and *Polygnathus*

PLATE 6. Species of *Neoprioniodus*, *Nothognathella*, *Ozarkodina*, *Pelekysgnathus*, *Polygnathellus*, *Prioniodina*, *Roundya*, *Sagittodontus*, *Scutula*, and *Spathognathodus* (All figures × 30 except 1, 2, 6, 20, and 22, which are × 34)

Figures

1, 14. *Pelekysgnathus planus* Sannemann, middle *P. triangularis* through lower *crepida* zones, figured specimens from samples C-19 and 21, Pilot Shale, Confusion Range, Utah (Figs. 5 and 7), USNM 144383, 144384

2. *Spathognathodus* sp., middle *dubia* ( = *asymmetrica?*) zone, Mary's Mountain, Nevada (Fig. 2), USNM 144492

3. *Polygnathellus?* sp., middle *dubia* ( = *asymmetrica?*) zone, Mary's Mountain, Nevada (Fig. 2), USNM 144388

4. *Spathognathodus gratiosus* (Stauffer), middle *dubia* ( = *asymmetrica?*) zone, Mary's Mountain, Nevada (Fig. 2), USNM 144489

5. *Polygnathellus* n. sp., middle *dubia* ( = *asymmetrica?*) zone, Mary's Mountain, Nevada (Fig. 2), USNM 144385

6, 13. *Neoprioniodus armatus* (Hinde), middle *dubia* ( = *asymmetrica?*) zone, Mary's Mountain, Nevada (Fig. 2), USNM 144346, 144347

7. *Sagittodontus* sp., middle *dubia* ( = *assymmetrica?*) zone, Mary's Mountain, Nevada (Fig. 2), USNM 144486

8. *Scutula venusta* Sannemann, middle *P. triangularis* zone, sample 21, Pilot Shale, Confusion Range, Utah (Fig. 7), USNM 144487

9. *Ozarkodina* sp., all zones, figured specimen from lower *crepida* zone, sample C-19, Pilot Shale, Confusion Range, Utah (Fig. 5), USNM 144357

10. *Ozarkodina immersa* (Hinde), middle *dubia* ( = *asymmetrica?*) zone, Mary's Mountain, Nevada (Fig. 2), USNM 144355

11. *Nothognathella angusta* Stauffer, lower *gigas* through *rhomboidea* zones, figured specimen from sample 12, Pilot Shale, Confusion Range, Utah (Fig. 7), USNM 144351

12. *Neoprioniodus abnormalis* (Stauffer), upper *P. triangularis* zone, sample 3, Pilot Shale, Confusion Range, Utah (Fig. 7), USNM 144345

15. *Neoprioniodus powellensis* (Stauffer), middle *P. triangularis* zone, sample 21, Pilot Shale, Confusion Range, Utah (Fig. 7), USNM 144348

16. *Scutula sinepennata* Ziegler, lower *gigas* zone, sample 12, Pilot Shale, Confusion Range, Utah (Fig. 7), USNM 144488

17. *Nothognathella abnormis* Branson and Mehl, lower *gigas* zone, sample 12, Pilot Shale, Confusion Range, Utah (Fig. 7), USNM 144350

18. *Nothognathella incurva* Branson and Mehl, lower *crepida* zone, sample C-19, Pilot Shale, Confusion Range, Utah (Fig. 5), USNM 144353

19. *Nothognathella reversa* Branson and Mehl, middle *P. triangularis* through lower *crepida* zones, figured specimen from sample 11, Pilot Shale, Confusion Range, Utah (Fig. 7), USNM 144354

20. *Roundya laminata* (Branson and Mehl), upper *P. triangularis* zone, sample 11, Pilot Shale, Confusion Range, Utah (Fig. 7), USNM 144484

21. *Prioniodina alternata* (Bassler), middle *dubia* ( = *asymmetrica?*) to upper *P. triangularis* zones, figured specimen from sample 11, Pilot Shale, Confusion Range, Utah (Fig. 7), USNM 144483

22. *Roundya* sp., lower *crepida* zone, sample C-19, Pilot Shale, Confusion Range, Utah (Fig. 5), USNM 144485

23. *Spathognathodus aculeatus* (Branson and Mehl), middle *costatus* zone, sample RS-20, Fitchville Formation, Rattlesnake Spur, Utah (Fig. 8), USNM 144490

24. *Neoprioniodus* sp., lower *crepida* zone, sample C-19, Pilot Shale, Confusion Range, Utah (Fig. 5), USNM 144349

PLATE 7.   Species of *Nothognathella*, *Palmatolepis*, and *Polygnathus*
(All figures × 30)

1, 2. *Palmatolepis? ziegleri* n. sp., middle *dubia* (=*asymmetrica?*) zone, holotype, lateral and
upper views, Mary's Mountain, Nevada (Fig. 2), USNM 144375

3, 8. *Polygnathus dengleri* Bischoff and Ziegler, middle *dubia* (=*asymmetrica?*) zone, Mary's
Mountain, Nevada (Fig. 2), USNM 144394 (specimen of Fig. 8 lost)

4. *Nothognathella condita* Branson and Mehl, upper *P. triangularis* zone, sample 11, Pilot
Shale, Confusion Range, Utah (Fig. 7), USNM 144352

5, 13. *Polygnathus ordinata* Bryant, middle *dubia* (=*asymmetrica?*) zone, Mary's Mountain,
Nevada (Fig. 2), USNM 144405, 144480

6, 9. *Polygnathus brevis* Miller and Youngquist, middle *dubia* (=*asymmetrica?*) zone, Mary's
Mountain, Nevada (Fig. 2), USNM 144390, 144391

7. *Polygnathus foliata* Bryant, middle *dubia* (=*asymmetrica?*) through lower *crepida* zone,
figured specimen from sample C-19, Pilot Shale, Confusion Range, Utah (Fig. 5),
USNM 144398

10. *Polygnathus linguiformis* Hinde, middle *dubia* (=*asymmetrica?*) zone, Mary's Mountain,
Nevada (Fig. 2), USNM 144401

11. *Polygnathus webbi* Stauffer, middle *dubia* (=*asymmetrica?*) zone, Mary's Mountain, Nevada
(Fig. 2), USNM 144482

12. *Palmatolepis rugosa trachytera* Ziegler, *velifera* zone, sample RS-5, Pinyon Peak Limestone,
Rattlesnake Spur, Utah (Fig. 8), BYU 1108

14, 15. *Polygnathus dubia dubia* Hinde (=*asymmetrica ovalis?* Ziegler and Klapper), *dubia* (=*asymmetrica?*) zone, Mary's Mountain, Nevada (Fig. 2), USNM 144395, 144396

16, 17. *Polygnathus cristata* Hinde, middle *dubia* (=*asymmetrica?*) zone, Mary's Mountain, Nevada
(Fig. 2), USNM 144392, 144393

18. *Polygnathus dubia asymmetrica* Bischoff and Ziegler (=*asymmetrica asymmetrica?*), middle
*dubia* (=*asymmetrica?*) zone, Mary's Mountain, Nevada (Fig. 2), USNM 144397

Species of *Lonchodina, Nothognathella, Ozarkodina, Palmatolepis, Polygnathellus*, and *Polygnathus*

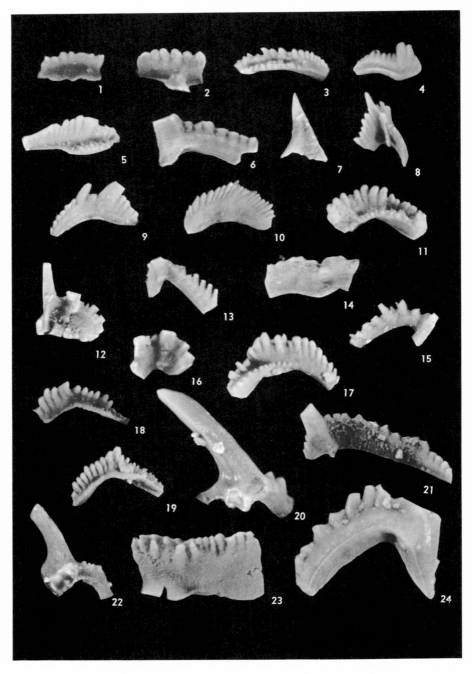

Species of *Neoprioniodus, Nothognathella, Ozarkodina, Pelekysgnathus, Polygnathellus, Prioniodina, Roundya, Sagittodontus, Scutula,* and *Spathognathodus*

PLATE 8.   Species of *Palmatolepis* and *Polygnathus*
(All figures × 42 except 13 and 15, which are × 30)

Figures

1, 2, 4, 5, 7, 10–12, 15. *Palmatolepis ? ziegleri* n. sp., middle *dubia* (=*asymmetrica?*) zone: 1, upper view, USNM 144377; 2, lateral view, USNM 144376; 4, upper view, USNM 144380; 5, upper-lateral view, USNM 144379; 7, upper-lateral and 11, lower views, holotype, USNM 144357; 10, upper-lateral and 12, lower views, USNM 144378; 15, lateral view, USNM 144382 (gerontic individual); all Mary's Mountain, Nevada (Fig. 2)

3, 14. *Palmatolepis foliacea* Youngquist, lower *gigas* zone, sample 12, Pilot Shale, Confusion Range, Utah (Fig. 7), UW 1005, 1006

6. *Palmatolepis coronata* Müller, middle *P. triangularis* zone, sample 21, Pilot Shale, Confusion Range, Utah (Fig. 7), UW 1007

8, 9. *Polygnathus dubia dubia* Hinde (=*asymmetrica ovalis?*), middle *dubia* (=*asymmetrica?*) zone, Mary's Mountain, Nevada (Fig. 2): 8, UW 1008, specimen transitional with *P. dengleri;* 9, UW 1009

13. *Palmatolepis hassi* Müller and Müller, upper *dubia* (=*asymmetrica?*) or lower *A. triangularis* zone, upper beds of Guilmette Formation, Confusion Range, Utah (Fig. 7), UW 1010

16. *Palmatolepis subperlobata* Branson and Mehl, middle *P. triangularis* zone, sample 21, Pilot Shale, Confusion Range, Utah (Fig. 7), UW 1011

PLATE 9. Species of *Palmatolepis*
(All figures × 30 except 6, 7, 9, 10, 12, which are × 42)

Figures

1, 4. *Palmatolepis quadrantinodosalobata* Sannemann, middle *P. triangularis* through lower *crepida* zones, figured specimens from sample 11, Pilot Shale, Confusion Range, Utah (Fig. 7), USNM 144362, 144363

2. *Palmatolepis minuta* Branson and Mehl, *rhomboidea* zone, sample E-1, Devils Gate Formation, Diamond Mountains, Nevada (Fig. 4), BYU 518

3. *Palmatolepis unicornis* Miller and Youngquist, lower *gigas* zone, sample 12, Pilot Shale, Confusion Range, Utah (Fig. 7), USNM 144374

5, 6, 12. *Palmatolepis subperlobata* Branson and Mehl, middle *P. triangularis* through *rhomboidea* zones, figured specimens as follows: 5, C-19; 6, 12, E-1, Pilot Shale, Confusion Range, Utah (Fig. 5), USNM 144366, and Devils Gate Formation, Diamond Mountains, Nevada (Figs. 6 and 12), USNM 144367, 144368

7, 13, 14. *Palmatolepis triangularis* Sannemann, *P. triangularis* to lower *crepida* zones, figured specimens as follows: 7, F-5; 13, C-19; 14, sample 11, Devils Gate Formation, Devils Gate Pass, Nevada (Fig. 3), and Pilot Shale, Confusion Range, Utah (Figs. 5 and 7), USNM 144371, 144372, 144373

8. *Palmatolepis glabra glabra* Ulrich and Bassler, *rhomboidea* zone, sample E-1, Devils Gate Formation, Diamond Mountains, Nevada (Fig. 4), BYU 521

9. *Palmatolepis subrecta* Miller and Youngquist, *gigas* zone, sample 2, young individual, Pilot Shale, Confusion Range, Utah (Fig. 7), USNM 144369

10. *Palmatolepis quadrantinodosa inflexa* Müller, lower *quadrantinodosa* zone, sample G-9, Pilot Shale, Burbank Hills, Utah (Fig. 6), USNM 144364

11. *Palmatolepis tenuipunctata* Sannemann, upper *P. triangularis* to lower *crepida* zones, figured specimen from sample C-19, Pilot Shale, Confusion Range, Utah (Fig. 5), USNM 144370

Species of *Nothognathella*, *Palmatolepis*, and *Polygnathus*

Species of *Palmatolepis* and *Polygnathus*

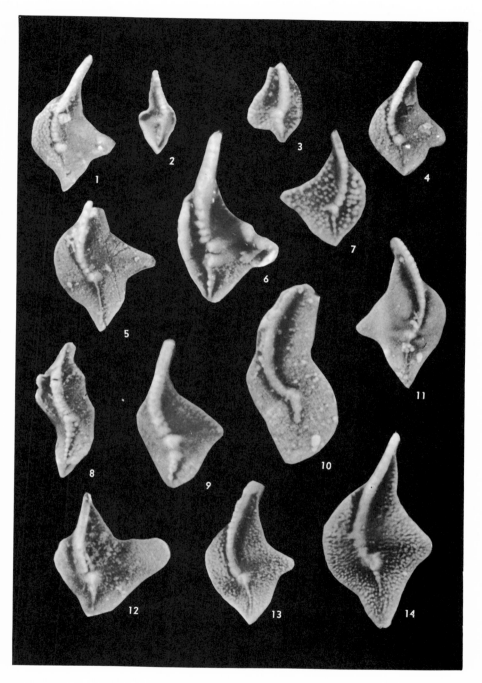

Species of *Palmatolepis*

# APPENDIX

## MEASURED SECTIONS

SECTION A: Locality shown on Figure 5. Measured section of Pilot Shale is about 5 miles northeast of intersection of dirt road shown on map. Section was measured about 1000 yards northwest of road where exposures are in a series of gullies. Only the lower part of the section is poorly exposed. Upper contact with Joana Limestone is distinct; lower contact with Guilmette Formation is partially covered.

|  | Thickness | |
|---|---|---|
| Top Pilot Shale | Interval | Cumulative |
| Shale, some calcareous, tan and black weathering, laminated to thin-bedded; few 1-foot beds of thin-bedded limestone . . . . . . . . | 258 | 258 |
| Limestone, shaly, dark brown, some places medium-bedded . . . . . | 28 | 286 |
| Shale and limestone, interbedded; shale dark gray to brown, thin-bedded; limestone, fine-grained, gray and brown, weathers tan, medium-bedded, some forming ledges . . . . . . . . . . . . . . . . | 197 | 483 |
| A-15 limestone, arenaceous, brown, weathers same . . . . . . . . | 1 | 484 |
| Limestone, fine-grained, dark brown to black, weathers gray, thin- to medium-bedded . . . . . . . . . . . . . . . . . . . . | 6 | 490 |
| Shale, dark brown, weathers gray and tan, thin-bedded, 200 feet of covered shale here . . . . . . . . . . . . . . . . . . . . | 344 | 834 |
| Limestone, fine-grained, dark gray, medium-bedded . . . . . . . . | 5 | 839 |
| Limestone, arenaceous, brown, weathers tan, thin- to medium-bedded . | 43 | 882 |
| Limestone, arenaceous, black, weathers tan to brown, medium-bedded . | 5 | 887 |
| Shale, black, thin-bedded; more than half of this interval is covered . . | 201 | 1088 |
| Guilmette Formation | | |

SECTION B: Locality shown on Figure 5. Measured section of Pilot Shale is about 0.25 mile northwest of road intersection shown on map. Section measured in gullies which cross Pilot strike valley at right angles. Upper contact with Joana Limestone is distinct; lower contact with Guilmette Formation is partially covered.

|  | Thickness | |
|---|---|---|
| Top Pilot Shale | Interval | Cumulative |
| Limestone, coarse-grained, gray to tan, weathers same, thin-bedded . . | 5 | 5 |
| Shale, some calcareous, gray and tan, thin-bedded, some calcareous siltstone forming ledges in middle of unit . . . . . . . . . . . | 134 | 139 |
| Limestone, brown, weathers tan, some interbeds of black shale . . . . | 64 | 203 |
| Limestone, fine-grained, dark gray, medium-bedded . . . . . . . . | 3 | 206 |
| Shale, gray to tan, weathers same, thin-bedded, some beds of fine-grained limestone. Some shale, calcareous . . . . . . . . . . . . . . | 317 | 523 |
| Covered . . . . . . . . . . . . . . . . . . . . . . . . . | 108 | 631 |
| Shale, tan and gray, weathers same, platy, laminated . . . . . . . . | 24 | 655 |
| Limestone, fine-grained, gray to brown, weathers lighter, medium-bedded | 15 | 670 |
| Shale, calcareous, brown, weathers tan, thin-bedded . . . . . . . . | 33 | 703 |
| Siltstone, brown, weathers yellow-brown, thin-bedded, half a foot of fine-grained gray limestone at top . . . . . . . . . . . . . . . | 37 | 740 |
| Shale, calcareous, brown, weathers tan, thin-bedded . . . . . . . . | 30 | 770 |
| Limestone, fine-grained, black, weathers brown, thin-bedded . . . . . | 209 | 979 |
| B-36 limestone, sandy, gray to brown, weathers orange brown, thin- to medium-bedded . . . . . . . . . . . . . . . . . . . . . | 18 | 987 |
| Limestone, black to brown, weathers brown, thin- to medium-bedded . | 78 | 1065 |
| Limestone, fine-grained, tan, weathers same, thin-bedded . . . . . . | 92 | 1157 |

| | | |
|---|---|---|
| B-34 limestone, arenaceous, gray, weathers tan, thin- to medium-bedded | 19 | 1176 |
| Limestone, fine-grained, black, weathers gray, medium-bedded . . . . | 37 | 1213 |

Guilmette Formation

SECTION C:   Locality shown on Figure 5. Measured section of Pilot Shale is about 0.25 mile northeast of section B in Pilot Shale strike valley; it is exposed in gullies that are at right angles to strike of valley. Upper contact with Joana Limestone and lower contact with Guilmette Formation are well exposed.

|  | Thickness | |
|---|---|---|
| Top Pilot Shale | Interval | Cumulative |
| Shale, calcareous, tan, weathers same, thin-bedded . . . . . . . . . | 75 | 75 |
| Siltstone, calcareous in part, dark gray to brown, weathers tan, ledge-former, medium-bedded . . . . . . . . . . . . . . . . . . | 20 | 95 |
| Shale, gray to tan, weathers lighter, thin-bedded . . . . . . . . . . | 81 | 176 |
| Shale, dark blue-gray, weathers tan to blue, thin-bedded . . . . . . | 60 | 236 |
| Shale and covered interval. Shale as previously mentioned and very thin-bedded . . . . . . . . . . . . . . . . . . . . . . . . . . | 449 | 685 |
| Limestone, fine-grained, blue-gray, weathers gray, thin- to medium-bedded . . . . . . . . . . . . . . . . . . . . . . . . . . | 25 | 710 |
| C-12 limestone, medium-grained, black, weathers gray, some fissile shale interbedded with medium beds of limestone . . . . . . . . . . | 51 | 761 |
| Siltstone and shale, calcareous, pink to tan, weathers tan, thin-bedded . | 37 | 798 |
| Covered interval . . . . . . . . . . . . . . . . . . . . . . . | 43 | 841 |
| Limestone, fine-grained, gray, weathers same, thin-bedded . . . . . . | 12 | 853 |
| Limestone, fine-grained, gray, weathers lighter, thick-bedded . . . . . | 12 | 865 |
| C-19 limestone, arenaceous, gray to black, weathers tan, thin- to medium-bedded . . . . . . . . . . . . . . . . . . . . . . . | 14 | 879 |
| Limestone, medium-grained, gray, weathers lighter, thin- to medium-bedded . . . . . . . . . . . . . . . . . . . . . . . . . . | 55 | 934 |
| Limestone, arenaceous, black, weathers gray, some thin beds which are partly covered, thicker beds well exposed above Guilmette . . . . | 170 | 1104 |

Guilmette Formation

SECTION F:   Locality shown on Figure 3. Measured section of the Devils Gate Limestone in outcrops along north side of highway. Upper contact with Pilot Shale well exposed. Lowest beds are lowest beds exposed at highway level, lower part of upper Devils Gate Limestone.

|  | Thickness | |
|---|---|---|
| Top Devils Gate Limestone | Interval | Cumulative |
| Limestone, fine-grained, gray to brown, weathers tan and dark gray, thin-bedded with some medium-bedded intervals . . . . . . . . | 77 | 77 |
| F-5 limestone, medium- to coarse-grained, gray to brown, weathers gray, medium-bedded . . . . . . . . . . . . . . . . . . . . . . . | 155 | 232 |
| F-6 limestone, fine-grained, dense, black, weathers dark gray, medium-bedded . . . . . . . . . . . . . . . . . . . . . . . . . . | 1 | 233 |
| Limestone, black to gray, some tan weathering, fine-grained, thin- and medium-bedded . . . . . . . . . . . . . . . . . . . . . . | 59 | 292 |
| Limestone, black, fine-grained, weathers gray to brown, massive-bedded | 35 | 327 |
| Limestone, fine-grained and shaly, dark gray, weathers brown and gray, thin-bedded . . . . . . . . . . . . . . . . . . . . . . . . . | 3 | 330 |
| Limestone, fine-grained, dark gray, weathers gray to brown, massive-bedded . . . . . . . . . . . . . . . . . . . . . . . . . . . | 21 | 351 |

| | Interval | Cumulative |
|---|---|---|
| Covered | 65 | 416 |
| F-15 limestone, fine-grained, laminated, black, weathers tan to gray, very thin-bedded | 12 | 428 |
| F-16 limestone, medium- and coarse-grained, black, weathers gray, mottled, thin- to medium-bedded | 163 | 591 |
| Limestone, some shale interbedded, fine- to medium-grained, black, weathers gray and brown, medium- and massive-bedded | 71 | 662 |
| Limestone, fine-grained, secondary calcite stringers prominent, dark gray, weathers same, thin- to medium-bedded | 62 | 724 |
| Limestone, fine-grained, some fossil hash, gray, weathers lighter, medium- and massive-bedded | 139 | 863 |
| F-24 limestone, medium- to coarse-grained, some fossil hash, medium gray, weathers blue-gray, medium-bedded | 37 | 900 |
| Limestone, fine-grained, shaly, gray, weathers same, thin-bedded | 9 | 909 |
| F-26 limestone, medium- to coarse-grained, gray, weathers light gray, massive beds at base separated by medium-bedded units, some fossil hash | 239 | 1148 |

SECTION G: Locality shown on Figure 6. Measured section of the Pilot Shale about 3 miles southwest of Utah 21, in Pilot valley. Upper contact with Joana Limestone is distinct; lower contact with Guilmette Formation is partially covered.

| Top Pilot Shale | Thickness Interval | Cumulative |
|---|---|---|
| Shale and limestone, interbedded, light gray, weathers gray to tan, nodular, thin-bedded, covered in part | 59 | 59 |
| Shale and limestone, interbedded, gray, weathers lighter, thin- to medium-bedded | 107 | 166 |
| Limestone, fine-grained, gray, weathers lighter, thin-bedded | 9 | 175 |
| C-6 limestone, arenaceous, light gray, weathers same, black "speckled" appearance on weathered surface, thin-bedded | 65 | 240 |
| Limestone, shaly in appearance, fine-grained, dense, gray to tan, weathers gray to dark gray, thin-bedded | 62 | 302 |
| Limestone, fine-grained, dark gray, weathers same, mottled appearance on weathered surface, thin- to medium-bedded | 75 | 377 |
| Limestone, fine-grained, dense, some beds sandy, gray to dark gray on fresh and weathered surface, medium-bedded | 125 | 502 |

SECTION RS: Locality shown on Figure 8. Measured section of the Pinyon Peak Limestone and lower Fitchville Formation on Rattlesnake Spur, East Tintic area, central Utah. Rattlesnake Spur is prominent projection from main mountains and west of Allens Ranch. Road leads to base and to south of spur. The formations are well exposed in continuous outcrops with the Pinyon Peak–Victoria Quartzite gradational contact exposed as are the Pinyon Peak–Fitchville and Fitchville–Gardison formation contacts. Contact of Pinyon Peak and Fitchville taken at first massive limestone beds above Victoria Quartzite. At this locality the contact is at the crest of a ridge and the basal beds of the Fitchville form a prominent ledge with the older Pinyon Peak beds in a saddle west of the ledge.

| Pinyon Peak Limestone | Thickness Interval | Cumulative |
|---|---|---|
| Limestone and dolomite, fine- to medium-grained, light gray, weathers same, thin-bedded, shaly zones between more resistant layers | 25 | 25 |
| Limestone, brown to gray, medium- and fine-grained, weathers gray. Some parts arenaceous, medium-bedded | 7 | 32 |

Limestone and shaly limestone, dark gray, fine-grained, weathers medium blue-gray, thin- to medium-bedded . . . . . . . . . .     10       42

RS-5 limestone, medium- to coarse-grained, medium gray, weathers same, fossil hash, medium-bedded (same unit as H-3 of Clark and Becker, 1960) . . . . . . . . . . . . . . . . . . . . . .     3       45

RS-6 limestone, coarse-grained, fossil hash, gray, weathers same, medium-bedded . . . . . . . . . . . . . . . . . . . . .     10       55

Limestone, fine-grained, dense, brown to gray, weathers tan to gray, medium-bedded. Some shaly limestones interbedded . . . . . .     23       78

RS-12 limestone, fine-grained, dark gray, weathers same, medium-bedded. Shale interbeds (same unit as H-1 of Clark and Becker, 1960) . . . . . . . . . . . . . . . . . . . . . . . . . . .     17       95

Fitchville Formation

Limestone, fine- to medium-grained, gray, weathers light gray, massive-bedded. *Syringopora* and other fossils . . . . . . . . . . . . . .     6       101

Limestone, lithology as above but beds are medium-bedded and not part of ridge . . . . . . . . . . . . . . . . . . . . . . . . . . . .     15       116

Limestone, medium- to coarse-grained, light gray, weathers same, medium- to massive-bedded . . . . . . . . . . . . . . . . .     8       124

RS-19, RS-20, 2 feet apart, limestone, fine- to medium-grained, gray, weathers lighter, medium-bedded . . . . . . . . . . . . . . .     4       128

Limestone, as in other units. Conodonts in limestones 30–50 feet higher in section contain Lower Mississippian guide, *Siphonodella* spp.

# INDEX

Page numbers in boldface represent detailed descriptions of taxa. Entries on locality, age, and author refer only to data not included in the systematic lists.